Cooperative Extension

Production of Vegetables, Strawberries, and Cut Flowers Using Plasticulture

Edited by
William J. Lamont, Jr.

Written by
John W. Bartok, Jr.
Robert D. Berghage
A. Richard Bonanno
Joseph A. Fiola
Stephen A. Garrison
James W. Garthe
George J. Hochmuth
Laurie Hodges
William J. Lamont, Jr.
Steve Olson
Michael D. Orzolek
James W. Paterson
David S. Ross
Robert Rouse
James Sellmer
Otho S. Wells

Natural Resource, Agriculture, and Engineering Service (NRAES)
Cooperative Extension
PO Box 4557
Ithaca, New York 14852-4557

NRAES–133
December 2004

ISBN 0-935817-87-5

Library of Congress Cataloging-in-Publication Data

Production of vegetables, strawberries, and cut flowers using plasticulture / edited by
    William J. Lamont, Jr. ; written by John W. Bartok, Jr. ... [et al.].
        p. cm. — (NRAES ; 133)
    "November 2004"—T.p. verso.
    Includes bibliographical references.
    ISBN 0-935817-87-5 (pbk.)
    1. Vegetables. 2. Strawberries. 3. Cut flowers. 4. Plastics in agriculture. I. Lamont,
William J., 1945– II. Bartok, John W., 1936– III. Natural Resource, Agriculture, and
Engineering Service. Cooperative Extension. IV. NRAES (Series) ; 133.

SB321.P679 2004
631.3—dc22   2004061033

Natural Resource, Agriculture, and Engineering Service (NRAES)
Cooperative Extension
PO Box 4557
Ithaca, New York 14852-4557
Phone: (607) 255-7654
Fax: (607) 254-8770
E-mail: NRAES@CORNELL.EDU
Web site: WWW.NRAES.ORG

Contents

Acknowledgments

The authors would like to thank the following peer reviewers, whose thoughtful comments helped increase the accuracy and usefulness of this book.

Arthur Amidon
President
Amidon Recycling
Wilton, New Hampshire

Robert G. Anderson
Professor
Department of Horticulture
University of Kentucky

Steve Clarke
*Rural/Environmental Engineer and Provincial Crop
   Engineering Specialist*
Ontario Ministry of Agriculture and Food

Doug Doohan
*Associate Professor and Extension Weed Specialist/
   Fruit and Vegetable Crops*
Department of Horticulture and Crop Science
The Ohio State University

Darbie M. Granberry
Professor
Department of Horticulture
Rural Development Center
University of Georgia

Robert Hochmuth
Multicounty Extension Agent/Vegetables
North Florida Research and Education Center
University of Florida

E. Jay Holcomb
Professor of Floriculture
Department of Horticulture
The Pennsylvania State University

Albert R. Jarrett
Professor of Agricultural Engineering
Department of Agricultural and Biological Engineering
The Pennsylvania State University

Wesley Kline
County Agricultural and Resource Management Agent
Rutgers Cooperative Extension

David E. Kopsell
Postdoctoral Research Scientist
Department of Plant Biology
University of New Hampshire

Brent Loy
Professor
Department of Plant Biology
University of New Hampshire

Bradley Majek
Extension Specialist in Weed Science
Rutgers Cooperative Extension

Frank Mangan
Extension Assistant Professor
Department of Plant and Soil Sciences
University of Massachusetts

Charles W. Marr
Professor of Horticulture
Department of Horticulture, Forestry, and Recreation
   Resources
Kansas State University

Charles A. McClurg
Emeritus Associate Professor
Department of Natural Resource Sciences and Landscape
   Architecture
University of Maryland

Charles O'Dell
Extension Horticulture Specialist Emeritus
Department of Horticulture
Virginia Polytechnic Institute and State University

E. Barclay Poling
Professor
Department of Horticultural Science
North Carolina State University

Anusuya Rangarajan
Associate Professor
Department of Horticulture
Cornell University

Douglas C. Sanders
Professor and Extension Specialist
Department of Horticultural Science
North Carolina State University

Robert L. Tjaden
*Assistant Director for Agriculture and Natural Resources
 Programs*
Maryland Cooperative Extension

Greg Welbaum
Professor
Department of Horticulture
Virginia Polytechnic Institute and State University

About the Authors

John W. Bartok, Jr.
Extension Professor Emeritus
Department of Natural Resources Management and
   Engineering
University of Connecticut

Robert D. Berghage
Associate Professor of Horticulture
Department of Horticulture
The Pennsylvania State University

A. Richard Bonanno
*Adjunct Professor and Extension Weed Management
   Specialist*
University of Massachusetts Extension

Joseph A. Fiola
*Regional Extension Specialist in Viticulture and Small
   Fruits*
Western Maryland Research and Education Center
Maryland Cooperative Extension

Stephen A. Garrison
Extension Specialist Emeritus in Vegetable Crops
New Jersey Agricultural Experiment Station
Rutgers Agricultural Research and Extension Center

James W. Garthe
Agricultural Engineer and Instructor
Department of Agricultural and Biological Engineering
The Pennsylvania State University

George J. Hochmuth
Professor of Horticultural Sciences and Center Director
North Florida Research and Education Center
University of Florida

Laurie Hodges
Associate Professor and Extension Specialist
Department of Agronomy and Horticulture
University of Nebraska–Lincoln

William J. Lamont, Jr.
Professor of Vegetable Crops
Department of Horticulture
The Pennsylvania State University

Steve Olson
Professor of Horticultural Sciences
North Florida Research and Education Center
University of Florida

Michael D. Orzolek
Professor of Vegetable Crops
Department of Horticulture
The Pennsylvania State University

James W. Paterson
Professor Emeritus
Rutgers University

David S. Ross
Professor
Department of Biological Resources Engineering
University of Maryland–College Park

Robert Rouse
*Regional Extension Specialist in Fruits and Vegetables
   (retired)*
Wye Research and Education Center
University of Maryland

James Sellmer
Associate Professor of Ornamental Horticulture
Department of Horticulture
The Pennsylvania State University

Otho S. Wells
Professor Emeritus
Department of Plant Biology
University of New Hampshire

CHAPTER 1

Plasticulture—An Overview

William J. Lamont, Jr.

The discovery and development of the polyethylene polymer in the late 1930s—and its subsequent introduction in the early 1950s in the form of plastic films, mulches, and drip irrigation tubing and tape—revolutionized the commercial production of selected vegetable crops, strawberries, and cut flowers and gave rise to plasticulture. The later discovery of other polymers, such as polyvinyl chloride, polypropylene, and polyesters, and their uses in pipes, fertigation equipment, filters, fittings, connectors, containers for growing transplants, picking and packaging containers, and row covers, further extended the use of plastic components in this production system.

Simply defined, plasticulture is a crop-growing system wherein significant benefits are achieved from using products derived from plastic polymers. A complete plasticulture system consists of plastic mulches, drip irrigation, fertigation/chemigation, soil sanitation (fumigation and solarization), windbreaks, stand-establishment technology, season-extension technology, integrated pest management, cropping strategies, post-harvest handling, and marketing (photo 1-1).

Photo 1-1. Complete plasticulture system: plastic mulch, drip irrigation, transplanted tomatoes, fertigation, annual rye windbreak, permanent tree windbreak.

To be competitive in today's marketplace, growers must strive continually for maximum high-quality economic yields and extended production cycles that include spring and fall crops. Plasticulture is a management tool that enables producers to realize greater returns per unit of land. Some of the benefits are:

- Earlier crop production (seven to 21 days earlier)
- Higher yields per acre (as much as two to three times higher)
- Cleaner and higher-quality products
- More efficient use of resources (water, fertilizer, labor, and so forth)
- Reduced leaching of fertilizers, especially on lighter sandy soils
- More efficient use of fertilizer inputs through fertigation technology
- Reduced soil erosion from wind and water
- Potential decrease in losses from disease
- Better management of certain insect pests
- Fewer weed problems
- Reduced soil compaction and elimination of root pruning
- Maximum efficiency through double- or triple-cropping

To realize the maximum benefits from plasticulture, growers need to integrate the individual components into a complete program. The plasticulture system can be used effectively on small or large acreages. The basic principles and intensive management required for success are the same, regardless of the size of operation.

A component list for a representative 20-acre plastic mulch/drip irrigation system is presented in table 1-1 (page 2). The system in table 1-1 has a pond as the water source and is zoned into four blocks of 5 acres each. In other words, 5 acres are watered at one time.

A smaller drip irrigation system for 2 acres would require a 5-horsepower pump, 15-inch-diameter sand filters, and less materials overall. The cost for a 2-acre system would be approximately $3,200 and could accommodate up to three additional 2-acre sections (watered at separate times) with an approximate additional cost of $600 per acre. This system has been used successfully to produce vegetables, strawberries, and cut flowers with significant increases in earliness, yield, and/or crop quality.

Vegetables that have shown significant increases in earliness and yield using plasticulture include muskmelon, tomato, pepper, cucumber, squash, eggplant, and watermelon (photo 1-2). Other crops, such as

TABLE 1-1
Component list for a 20-acre plasticulture system

COMPONENT DESCRIPTION	QUANTITY	UNIT	UNIT PRICE ($)	TOTAL PRICE ($)
Engine and pump (14-horsepower engine, Berkley pump)	1	each	4,000.00	4,000.00
24" media filter and fertilizer injector	pair	each	3,200.00	3,200.00
Layflat, header pipe 4"	1,800	feet	1.01	1,818.00
Layflat, header pipe 3"	1,500	feet	0.81	1,215.00
Drip tape (7,500'/roll)	20	roll	135.00	2,700.00
Plastic mulch (1.0 mil black embossed 4,000'/roll)	40	roll	80.00	3,200.00
Zone control/pressure-regulation valve, 3"	4	each	180.00	720.00
Insert tee, 4"	1	each	31.62	31.62
PVC tee (S x T), 4" x 3"	4	each	14.34	57.36
Insert ell, 4"	2	each	21.25	42.50
Insert x slip adapter, 4"	6	each	11.26	67.56
PVC bushing, 4" x 2"	2	each	5.35	10.70
PVC tee (S x T), 3"	4	each	10.87	43.48
PVC nipple, 3" x 4"	8	each	5.52	44.16
Insert x slip adapter, 3"	8	each	8.92	71.36
Insert male adapter, 3"	8	each	5.30	42.40
PVC ell (S x T), 3"	8	each	6.80	54.40
PVC bushing, 3" x 2"	8	each	2.28	18.24
PVC nipple, 2" x 4"	10	each	1.49	14.90
Air-release valve, 2"	10	each	27.00	270.00
PVC ell, 2"	2	each	1.38	2.76
Hose clamp, 4"	14	each	1.72	24.08
Hose clamp, 3"	16	each	1.47	23.52
Tape x layflat connectors	480	each	0.95	456.00
Layflat holepunch	2	each	75.00	150.00
Subtotal				18,277.04
Sales tax 1%				182.77
Total				18,459.81

SOURCE: Henry Johnson, Johnson Irrigation Co., Advance, North Carolina, 2002.

NOTE: Only plastic mulch and drip irrigation components are included. The plan assumes a level field with a surface water supply (pond) adjacent to the field. The filters designed in this system have the capacity to irrigate 5 acres at one time. The system is basic with media filters, a venturi injector, and a 14-horsepower engine and pump. Additional equipment that should be considered includes secondary filters, additional pressure regulators, pressure gauges, and water meters. Water samples and field topography should be analyzed before actual drip design. Sales tax, freight, and field labor were not included in the estimate.

Photo 1-2. Peppers grown using plasticulture have shown significant increases in earliness and yield.

sweet corn, snap beans, pumpkins and decorative gourds, cole crops, okra, potatoes, and herbs, have shown similar responses and may lend themselves to double- or triple-cropping strategies. Some yields of various vegetable crops using plasticulture are presented in table 1-2.

TABLE 1-2
Yields of selected vegetables using plasticulture

CROP	YIELDS/ACRE
Eastern muskmelon	8,000–9,000 fruit at 4–6 pounds/fruit
Western muskmelon	12,000–15,000 fruit at 3–4 pounds/fruit
Eggplant	1,000–1,200 bushels (33 pounds/bushel)
Cucumber	1,200 bushels (55 pounds/bushel)
Onions	40,000 pounds
Pepper	1,600 bushels (25 pounds/bushel)
Squash	800 bushels (45 pounds/bushel)
Tomato	3,200 boxes (20 pounds/box)
Watermelon	3,000 fruit

Plastic Mulches

Plastic mulches have been used commercially on vegetables since the early 1960s. Much of the early university research before 1960 concerned the impact of color (black and clear) on soil and air temperature, moisture retention, and vegetable yields (Emmert 1957). Most plastic mulches used in the United States are made of linear low- or high-density polyethylene and are 0.5–1.25 mils thick, 48–60 inches wide, and on rolls 2,000–4,800 feet long, depending on the thickness of mulch. The linear high-density polyethylene is used to reduce weight and cost and is stronger than the same thickness of low-density polyethylene. The plastic mulch is either slick (smooth) or embossed with a diamond-shaped pattern (photo 1-3). This embossed pattern helps reduce expansion and contraction, which can contribute to the loosening of the mulch from the raised bed. The raised bed is generally 4–6 inches high and 30 inches wide with the center 1.25 inches higher than the edge. Soil under a raised bed will warm up faster in the spring and will shed excess water from the bed into row middles, thus keeping the plants drier and preventing deterioration in product quality from contact between harvestable portions of the plants and wet soil or standing water.

Photo 1-3. Raised bed 4–6 inches high, 30 inches wide with the center 1.25 inches higher than the edge, covered with embossed black plastic mulch.

Drip Irrigation

Drip irrigation is another cornerstone in a plasticulture production system (photo 1-4, page 4). It should be used with plastic mulch to obtain the greatest benefit of the mulch. Water savings with drip irrigation can amount to as much as 80% compared to other irrigation methods (Bogle and Hartz 1986). Double- or triple-cropping by fertilizing successive crops through the drip irrigation tape or tubing using a fertilizer proportioner also contributes to improved economic returns, as it allows greater production from the investment in plastic mulch and drip irrigation equipment.

Photo 1-4. Drip irrigation is a cornerstone of the plasticulture system.

The major components of a drip irrigation system are (1) drip tubes or drip tapes; (2) filters—media, screen, or disc; (3) pressure regulators—spring or valve; (4) valves—hand-operated, hydraulic, or electric; (5) pressure gauges; (6) water meters—flow or totalizing; (7) injectors—for introducing chemicals and fertilizers into the irrigation system; and (8) controllers—from simple time clocks to complex computer-controlled units that run many zones.

Because vegetables, strawberries, and cut flowers are often planted in rows, a drip tube or tape is used to wet a continuous strip along the row. A wide variety of drip tapes are available that vary in thickness, outlet hole spacing, water flow rates, and diameter (photo 1-5). Current drip tape manufacturers are listed in appendix A, page 123.

The source of the water supply for drip irrigation is extremely important and can include wells, ponds, lakes, municipal lines, or pits. Well-water sources generally are fairly clean and may require only a simple screen or disc filter to remove particles. It is very important to determine whether precipitates or other contaminants in the water could plug the tiny outlet openings. A water analysis is essential before installing a drip system. Municipal sources generally provide documentation of water quality, which makes it easier to anticipate potential problems.

Surface water such as streams, ponds, pits, or rivers may contain silt, sand, bacteria, algae, or other aquatic life. Consequently, agricultural sand media filters are an absolute necessity with surface water (photo 1-6). These filters are generally more expensive than screen or disc filters.

Photo 1-6. Agricultural sand media filters on mobile pumping unit used to filter pond water for drip irrigation.

Securing assistance from an irrigation dealer or professional familiar with drip irrigation system design and installation is strongly recommended and can be very helpful in avoiding potential future problems. Other major considerations are crop water management, which is extremely dependent on soil type and stage of crop growth, and maintenance of the drip irrigation system.

Fertigation

Once a drip irrigation system has been installed, it makes economic and environmental sense to fertilize the crop via the drip system as needed. When done properly, this results in more efficient use of fertilizers and probably lessens the potential for groundwa-

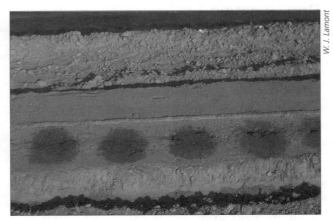

Photo 1-5. Wetting pattern of buried drip irrigation tape with 12-inch spacing between emitter holes.

ter contamination through leaching of fertilizers below the plant root zone (Hochmuth 1992).

In its broadest sense, fertigation is defined as feeding a crop by injecting soluble fertilizers into water in the irrigation system. A variety of methods are available to introduce chemicals into a drip system, including pumps (small electric-powered pumps or pumps powered by the irrigation water), venturis, pressure differential tanks, bladder tanks, and gravity (photo 1-7). Each system can employ a different method or a combination of methods to better suit each situation. For fertigation to be successful, irrigation scheduling must be coordinated closely with the nutrient needs of the crop (Clark et al. 1991). To be a good fertigator, a grower first must be a good irrigator.

Photo 1-7. Small venturi unit used for fertigation.

Soil Sanitation

Soil sanitation is practiced in many production areas, especially the southeastern United States and California. Plastic mulches are used either with chemical fumigants or as covers during soil solarization. When fumigants are applied in rows or strips, the amount of material actually applied on an acre will depend on the row width and will be a percentage of the broadcast rate. The temperature of the soil should be at least 50°F, and soil should be well worked, free from undecomposed plant debris, and have adequate moisture for seed germination. If the weather and soil are warm, the fumigant should escape through the plastic mulch in 12–14 days (photo 1-8). Fumigation is used primarily for nematode control, but by using a multipurpose fumigant, it can provide good control of soilborne diseases as well (Scoville and Leaman 1965).

Photo 1-8. Soil fumigation while applying the plastic mulch and drip irrigation tape.

Soil solarization is another method of reducing losses from soil pests. It is a hydrothermal method of soil deinfestation that occurs in moist soil covered by mulch film (usually clear) and exposed to sunlight during the hot summer months (Stapleton 1991).

Windbreaks

Windbreaks, whether permanent (trees) or annual (small grains), are an important but often overlooked component of a plasticulture system. A combination of permanent and annual windbreaks can modify wind profiles and influence temperatures and other microclimate features (Hodges et al. 1994). It is important to note that windbreaks can serve as habitat for both beneficial and pest insects (Dix and Leatherman 1988).

Windbreaks consisting of strips of winter wheat, rye, or barley can be established to protect young plantings from prevailing winds (photo 1-9). For

Photo 1-9. Rye grain windbreak every five rows of plastic mulch protects early-planted muskmelons.

maximum effectiveness, the grain strips should be planted in the fall in most areas of the United States. Each grain strip should be 10–12 feet wide, with strips far enough apart to accommodate five or six mulched beds on 5- to 6-foot centers. Topdressing the strips in the spring helps to ensure a dense foliar growth of the grain.

Another option is to broadcast-seed a grain cover crop in the fall. It is important to till the crop area early enough in spring so that cover crop debris will not interfere with application of the plastic mulch and drip irrigation. Once wind protection is no longer required, the grain strips can be mowed and used as drive rows for pesticide applications and harvesting.

Stand-Establishment Technology

Crop establishment in a plasticulture system involves either transplanting or direct-seeding. Well-grown, containerized transplants are integral parts of this production system. Information on the production of high-quality transplants is readily available from any state extension service.

Transplants can be set by hand or machines with single- or multi-row units. See appendix A (page 123) for some current manufacturers of mechanical and water-wheel transplanters.

The following vegetables have been transplanted successfully into plasticulture systems: tomato, pepper, eggplant, watermelon, muskmelon, honeydew, summer squash, cucumber, onion, and okra (photo 1-10). In specialty or niche marketing situations, other crops such as sweet corn, herbs, leaf lettuce, and cole crops can be transplanted as well as strawberries and cut flowers.

Mechanical seeders are available in single- or multi-row models that will plant directly through the plastic mulch. This equipment is good for direct-seeded crops such as sweet corn and cucumbers as well as other crops. See appendix A (page 123) for manufacturers.

Season-Extension Technology

Vegetables, strawberries, and cut flowers all benefit from using season-extending technology such as row covers, low tunnels, and high tunnels. These technologies promote earliness by creating a mini greenhouse effect. Row covers also provide a physical barrier that excludes insect pests and protects the crop in the early stages of growth (Natwick and Durazo 1985).

The first row covers used were solid polyethylene sheeting that needed support and required venting during the day (Hall and Besemer 1972). To eliminate the need for manual venting, a variety of materials have been developed, including slit polyethylene covers that require wire hoops, floating nonwoven sheets, white point-bonded polypropylene material, spunbonded polyester fabrics, polypropylene, and polyethylene sheets with tiny pores (photo 1-11). See appendix A, page 123, for a list of manufacturers.

High tunnels or minimally heated protective structures are another option in a plasticulture system (photo 1-12). They can be used to extend the spring and fall growing seasons and even allow winter pro-

Photo 1-10. Tomato transplants set on plastic mulch with a waterwheel transplanter.

Photo **1-11.** Floating row covers used to protect an early-planted crop.

Photo 1-12. High tunnels are used to extend the growing season and in some locations permit winter production.

duction of certain vegetable crops. High tunnels are covered with a single layer of polyethylene film (Wells 1991). The use of high tunnels is widespread in many parts of the world, especially in Asia, Spain, and Italy.

Pest Management

Another component of the plasticulture system is the integration of insect, disease, and weed control that involves the use of biological as well as chemical management measures. As in nonplasticulture growing systems, an integrated pest management (IPM) approach should be used that combines the use of disease-resistant varieties, chemical and biological control practices, crop rotation, effective scouting of fields, and other recommended practices.

Only approved herbicides should be used between rows of mulched plastic beds, because this area is not considered fallow. The use of low-pressure sprayers coupled with shielded application of herbicides is recommended. This approach will reduce the application of the herbicide material on the plastic bed, which could result in potential crop injury from increased concentration of herbicides in the planting holes (Bonanno 1996).

Reflective plastic mulches, like silver-faced plastic mulch, have been shown to interfere with the movement of aphids, which often vector virus diseases to various vegetable crops [such as watermelon mosaic virus II, which causes green streaks in summer squash (Lamont et al. 1990) and mottling and green streaks in yellow squash, melons, and pumpkins].

Cropping Strategies: Double- or Triple-Cropping

Although it may be somewhat limited in the Northeast, double- or triple-cropping is certainly another important component of the plasticulture system. With such a strategy, producers can grow the equivalent of 2 or 3 acres of produce on 1 acre of land using the plasticulture system inputs (plastic mulch, drip tape) already in place.

Cropping sequences such as one in Kansas that involved broccoli or cabbage followed by yellow summer squash, which was then followed by broccoli, cabbage, or Chinese cabbage (Marr and Lamont 1992), and another in Maryland that involved successful production of annual hill strawberries followed by muskmelons (Lamont and Poling 1986), may stimulate some growers to try other combinations (photo 1-13). Also, in the event that the first crop is a failure, double- or triple-cropping is a potential means of recouping investments in inputs like plastic mulch, drip tape or tubing, and fertilizer. Fertigating through the drip system makes it relatively easy to supply sufficient nutrients to a second or third crop. Some suggested spring–fall sequences are shown in table 1-3 (page 8).

Photo 1-13. Muskmelons following annual hill strawberries.

Marketing

Because plasticulture provides an opportunity to produce much higher overall yields earlier in the season, producers should have their marketing strategies and outlets as refined as possible before planting any crop. By converting bare-ground acreage to plasticulture,

TABLE 1-3

Suggested spring–fall crop sequences for double- or triple-cropping

SPRING	FALL
Pepper	Summer squash, cucumber, cole crops
Tomato	Cucumber, summer squash, cole crops
Summer squash	Pumpkin, tomato, cole crops
Eggplant	Summer squash
Cucumber	Tomato, pumpkin, summer squash
Muskmelon	Tomato
Watermelon	Tomato
Honeydew	Tomato
Cole crops	Summer squash, pumpkin, muskmelon, tomato
Lettuce	Summer squash, pumpkin, muskmelon, tomato
Snap bean	Summer squash, pumpkin, muskmelon, tomato
Sweet corn	Summer squash, tomato, okra, cucumber
Strawberry	Tomato, summer squash, cucumber, muskmelon, pumpkin, okra

the potential earliness and increases in total yield could present a marketing challenge if producers are not properly prepared.

Plasticulture can be used as a marketing tool. For example, muskmelons, strawberries, or cut flowers grown using plasticulture can be marketed in advertisements and on individual boxes with the following statement: "These crops grown using plastic mulch and drip irrigation." This form of advertisement promotes product quality and environmental awareness to buyers and consumers.

Disposal of Used Plastics

One question that is always asked by people who are interested in or are using plastics is, What do I do with the plastics when I am done using them? Disposal of used plastic material is a concern not only in the United States but also worldwide. There have been many attempts at solving the problem, such as the development and use of photodegradable or biodegradable materials that disappear over time; plastic reuse, which reduces the amount disposed; reducing the weight of films; recycling; and incineration (Hemphill 1993).

Mulch films and drip irrigation tapes are by far the hardest components of plasticulture to deal with because, after a season in the field, these materials contain plant debris, dirt, and moisture, which interfere with recycling. Another option is to incinerate them to recover their very substantial fuel value: a pound of plastics has nearly as much potential heat energy as an equivalent amount of fuel oil. Used plastics have been burned in waste-to-energy plants. Another incineration option being explored by researchers at The Pennsylvania State University is to create a "fuel nugget" that can be burned as a supplement to coal or other waste products or by itself in a heating system designed for many types of structures (photo 1-14).

Photo 1-14. Fuel nugget or Plastofuel derived from used agricultural plastics.

More investigation is needed to refine the collection, preparation, and transportation of plastics from the site of use to the point where they are processed further and then to the point of incineration. Incineration may be at least one answer to the disposal problem, but much more work is needed before this can be considered the final solution.

Summary

Plasticulture is a production system that involves high input costs and levels of management and is subject to mismanagement and risk (just as any production system is). However, with proper planning, attention to details, and dedication to all aspects of the plasticulture system, the opportunity exists to reduce the acreage of an existing operation and possibly increase profits using efficient production techniques.

CHAPTER 2

Plastic Mulches

William J. Lamont, Jr.

Plasticulture, as defined in chapter 1, is a crop-growing system wherein significant benefits are achieved from using products derived from plastic polymers. Plastic mulches, an essential component of plasticulture, have been used in commercial vegetable production since the early 1960s, and their usage is still increasing throughout the world. Plastic mulches offer many advantages, such as increased yields, earlier-maturing crops, higher-quality crops, enhanced insect management, and weed control. They also allow other plasticulture components, such as drip irrigation, to achieve maximum efficiency.

Although a variety of vegetables can be grown successfully using plastic mulches, muskmelons, tomatoes, peppers, cucumbers, squash, eggplant, watermelons, and okra have shown the most significant responses (photo 2-1). The production of strawberries and cut flowers is also greatly improved with plasticulture.

Photo 2-1. Staked tomatoes grown on red mulch.

Materials

The type of mulch to use will depend on which crops are to be grown, what season of the year it is, whether double- or triple-cropping will be practiced, and whether insect management is desired. Much of the early research on plastic mulches for vegetable production aimed to define the impact that different colors of mulches have on soil and air temperatures, moisture retention, and vegetable yields. Because of this research, three main colors of mulch predominate commercial vegetable production today—black, clear, and white (although white has largely been replaced by a coextruded white-on-black).

Most plastic mulches used in the United States are from 0.5 to 1.25 mils thick, are from 48 to 60 inches wide, and come on rolls 2,000–4,000 feet long. The width of the plastic mulch varies with the crop and cropping system. The plastic mulch will be either smooth or embossed with a diamond-shaped pattern that helps reduce expansion and contraction, which can loosen the mulch from the raised bed.

Plastic mulches directly affect the microclimate around the plant by modifying the radiation budget (absorptivity versus reflectivity) of the surface and decreasing the soil water loss (Liakatas et al. 1986, Tanner 1974). The color of a mulch largely determines its energy-radiating behavior and its influence on the microclimate around a vegetable plant. Color affects the surface temperature of the mulch and the underlying soil temperature. Ham and Kluitenberg (1994) found that the degree of contact between the mulch and soil or the tautness of the mulch greatly influences performance. If an air space is created between the plastic mulch and the soil by a rough soil surface, soil warming can be less effective than would be expected.

Black Mulches

The soil temperature under a plastic mulch depends on the thermal properties (reflectivity, absorptivity, or transmittancy) of a particular material in relation to incoming solar radiation (Schales and Sheldrake 1963). Black plastic mulch, the predominant color used in vegetable production, is an opaque blackbody absorber and radiator (photo 2-2). This means that black mulch absorbs most ultraviolet (UV), visible, and infrared (IR) wavelengths of incoming solar radiation and reradiates absorbed energy in the form of thermal radiation (heat), also called long-wavelength infrared radiation. Much of the solar energy absorbed by black plastic mulch is lost to the atmosphere through radiation and forced convection. The efficiency with which black mulch increases soil temperature can be improved by optimizing conditions for transferring heat from the mulch to the soil. Because thermal conductivity of the soil is high relative to that of air, much of the energy absorbed by black plastic can be transferred to soil by conduction if contact is good between the plastic mulch and the soil surface. The soil temperature under black plastic mulch during the daytime is generally 5°F higher at a 2-inch depth and 3°F higher at a 4-inch depth than that of bare soil.

Clear Mulches

In contrast, clear plastic mulch absorbs little solar radiation but transmits 85–95%, with relative transmission depending on the thickness and degree of opacity of the polyethylene. The undersurface of clear plastic mulch is usually covered with condensed water drop-lets. This water is transparent to incoming short-wave radiation but is opaque to outgoing long-wave infrared radiation, so much of the heat lost to the atmosphere from a bare soil by infrared radiation is retained by clear plastic mulch. Thus, the daytime soil temperature under clear plastic mulch is generally 8°–14°F higher at a 2-inch depth and 6°–9°F higher at a 4-inch depth than that of bare soil. Clear plastic mulches generally are used in the cooler regions of the United States, such as the New England states. Using clear plastic mulch will require the use of herbicides, soil fumigants, or solarization to control weeds.

White and Other Reflective Mulches

White, coextruded white-on-black (photo 2-3), or metallized silver reflective mulches can result in a slight decrease in soil temperature (−2°F at a 1-inch depth or −0.7°F at a 4-inch depth compared to bare soil), because they reflect back into the plant canopy most of the incoming solar radiation (Ham et al. 1993). These mulches can be used to establish a crop when soil temperatures are high and any reduction in soil temperature is beneficial. Depending on the degree of opacity of the white mulch, it may require the use of a fumigant or herbicide because of the potential for weed growth.

Wavelength-Selective Mulches

Another family of mulches is the wavelength-selective or photoselective mulches, which warm up the soil like clear mulch and suppress weed growth like black mulch (Loy et al. 1989). These mulches absorb

Photo 2-2. Muskmelons grown on black plastic mulch and clear plastic mulch.

Photo 2-3. Fall-planted broccoli transplants established on white-on-black coextruded mulch film.

photosynthetically active radiation (PAR), the radiation used in photosynthesis, and transmit solar infrared radiation (IR), thus providing a compromise between black and clear mulches. Such infrared-transmitting (IRT) mulches afford the weed-control properties of black mulch but are intermediate between black and clear mulch in terms of increasing soil temperature. The color of these mulches can be blue-green or brown. See appendix A (page 123) for manufacturers.

Response of Specific Crops to Mulch Color

The information below regarding the response of different crops to mulch color is based on ten years of research at The Pennsylvania State University's Horticulture Research Farm at Rock Springs, Pennsylvania.

Some generalities concerning insect response to mulch color can be made: (1) metallized silver repels aphids, (2) blue attracts thrips and has been very effective in greenhouse tomato production, and (3) yellow attracts insects. There also appears to be some reduction in disease pressure with crops grown on specific colors.

Tomato. This crop appears to respond more to red mulch than black, with an average 15% increase in marketable fruit yield over a three-year period. There appears to be a reduction in the incidence of early blight in plants grown on red mulch compared to plants grown on black mulch. When environmental conditions for plant growth are ideal, tomato response to red mulch is minimal.

Pepper. This crop appears to respond more to metallized silver mulch than black, with an average 20% increase in marketable fruit yield and fruit size over a three-year period. The lowest yields of marketable pepper were harvested from plants grown on either white or light blue mulch at the research location. Pepper plants grown on green infrared-transmitting mulch had similar marketable fruit yields compared to plants grown on black.

Eggplant. This crop appears to respond more to red mulch than black, with an average 12% increase in marketable fruit yield over a two-year period. The greatest response of eggplant to red mulch was observed when plants were growing under stress conditions (temperature and water). There also may be a varietal response of eggplant to the use of plastic mulch.

Muskmelon. This crop appears to respond more to green infrared-transmitting or dark blue mulch than black, with an average 35% increase in marketable fruit yield over a three-year period. The lowest yields of marketable muskmelon were harvested from plants grown on either white or black mulch.

Cucumber. This crop appears to respond more to dark blue mulch than black, with an average 30% increase in marketable fruit yield over a three-year period. There was a difference in yield response between an open-pollinated and a hybrid variety. The lowest yields of marketable cucumber were harvested from plants grown on yellow mulch at the research location.

Summer Squash. This crop appears to respond more to dark blue mulch than black, with an average 20% increase in marketable fruit yield over a two-year period. The lowest yield of marketable zucchini squash was harvested from plants grown on yellow mulch.

Onion. This crop appears to respond more to several different mulch colors including red, metallized silver, and black compared to no plastic mulch, with an average 24% increase in marketable bulb yield over eight varieties. There was a significant difference in yield response between specific onion varieties and mulch color. This trial evaluated red onions, but other onion types should respond similarly to the red onion varieties grown in this mulch trial.

Potato. This crop appears to respond more to several different mulch colors including red, metallized silver, and black compared to no plastic mulch, with an average 24% increase in marketable tuber yield. While there was no significant difference in yield response among the mulch colors, potatoes grown on the metallized silver mulch had the highest marketable tuber yields, coolest soil temperature, and least number of Colorado potato beetle adults. There was a significant difference in yield response between specific potato varieties and mulch color.

Photodegradable Mulch

Photodegradable plastic mulch is one alternative to conventional plastic mulches and their retrieval and disposal problems (Ennis 1987). Although photodegradable plastic looks very much like other plastic mulches when it is installed, it is broken down by ultraviolet sunlight. The actual rate of breakdown depends on several factors, including temperature, the proportion of the plastic shaded by the crop, and the amount of sunlight received during the growing season. When using photodegradable plastic mulch, keep in mind that decomposition of the buried edges (commonly referred to as the tuck) is initiated by lifting them out of the soil and exposing them to sunlight.

Research has also been conducted on a photodegradable mulch overlay system, in which the top layer of black photodegradable mulch degrades and increases the exposure of a white nondegradable layer (Graham et al. 1995). This particular change would lower the soil temperature later in the growing season. The potential use for this would be in a double-cropping system, where the same mulch is used for spring and fall crops (such as bell peppers planted in the spring followed by squash in late summer). The concept could be pursued further with several color changes during the season. The color changes would be accomplished by having more than one coextruded layer of differently pigmented photodegradable plastic on top of the nondegradable mulch. This concept is still in the developmental stage.

Other Material Considerations

An aboveground spectral response exists in addition to the response to elevated soil temperatures, and this response may be physiochemical (such as phytochrome regulation) or radiative (such as increasing or decreasing the heat load on the foliage). For example, in a pepper canopy, twice as much reflected photosynthetically active radiation (PAR) was measured above clear plastic mulch than above black plastic or bare soil (Cebula 1995). In other research, red and black plastics raised soil temperatures similarly, but higher early yields and less foliage were observed in plants grown on red plastic. Both red and black mulches reflected about the same amount of PAR, but red plastic increased the ratio of red:far-red wavelengths (R:FR) in the reflected light (Decoteau et al. 1988, 1989). The R:FR ratio and the amount of blue light reflected toward the canopy apparently are critical. In turnips, blue and green mulches induced longer leaves and higher shoot-to-root ratios than white mulch. The R:FR ratio reflected from white plastic is lower than that of sunlight. Other colors currently being investigated are red, blue, yellow, gray, and orange, which have distinct optical characteristics and thus reflect different radiation patterns into the canopy of a crop, thereby affecting plant growth and development (photo 2-4) (Decoteau et al. 1989, Orzolek and Murphy 1993). In a study by Loy et al. (1998), differences in reflectivity among red, black, and red-on-black mulches were minimal at 16 inches above the mulch surface and on the shaded side of the row. They speculate that for red mulch reflectivity to have a more sustained and more consistent effect on biomass accumulation and yield in tomato, the rows may need to be oriented in a north–south direction.

Photo 2-4. A wide variety of colored mulches are being investigated.

Light reflectivity can also affect insect response to the plants grown on the mulch. Yellow, red, and blue mulches have been shown to increase green peach aphid populations (Orzolek and Murphy 1993), and yellow mulch attracts striped and spotted cucumber beetles and Colorado potato beetles. (Yellow has long been used in greenhouses to monitor insect populations.) Mulches with a printed silver surface color have been shown to repel certain aphid species and reduce or delay the incidence of aphid-borne viruses in summer squash (Lamont et al. 1990). Similar to a white mulch, the degree of opacity of a gray mulch may require the use of herbicides or fumigants to prevent weed growth.

Some of these colored mulches (blue and red) had a dramatic impact on soil temperatures, raising them to 167°F (blue mulch) and 168°F (red mulch) at the 2-inch depth when the ambient air temperature was 104°F (Lamont, unpublished data from Kansas). Once the crop canopy covers the surface of the mulch bed (or shades the bed surface), soil temperatures among different mulch colors are approximately equal. More research still needs to be done on the effect that different colors have on crop growth and yields.

Application and Installation Techniques

Once the mulch has been selected, ensuring that it is applied properly is extremely important. In commercial production, the mulch is usually applied by machine. Three basic operations are involved in application: (1) bedding the soil, (2) pressing the bed, and (3) laying the plastic mulch and drip tube. A fourth operation is fumigating (if needed). These can be accomplished as separate operations or in combination, depending on the tractor horsepower and personal preference.

Bedding and Pressing the Soil

Several bedding machines are available to growers in single- and multiple-row models. With "super bedders," the soil is raised and then bedded in one operation

(photo 2-5). In other situations, the soil is first raised in one operation with hilling discs or double-disc hillers on a tool bar. The bed is then compressed to a uniform height and density using a bed press pan. The bedded rows should be spaced on 5- and 6-foot centers, depending on the equipment. A bed 4–6 inches high and 30 inches wide with a slope from the center to the edge of 1.25 inches is used commonly for vegetable production. The slope will allow excess rainfall to run off the mulch.

W. J. Lamont

Photo 2-5. Bedding the soil, pressing the soil, and applying the metallized silver mulch film and drip irrigation tape all in one operation.

Laying the Mulch and Drip Tube and Fumigating (If Required)

The soil must have adequate moisture for seed germination when plastic mulch is laid. Temperatures should be at least 50°F, and the soil should be well worked and, if using a fumigant, free from undecomposed plant debris. Researchers have been exploring the potential for delivering a fumigant via the drip irrigation system, not only to resanitize the area under the mulch cover between successive crops but to actually kill the first crop. Depending on soil temperature and the fumigant used, it could take anywhere from 12 days to four weeks for the fumigant to escape from under the plastic mulch.

Take time to adjust the machine so that the press wheels hold the plastic firmly against the bed and the covering discs place soil halfway up the side of the bed but not on top. Also, when starting applications, an-

DISPOSAL

Disposal continues to be a problem with plastic mulches and drip irrigation tape or tubing that are not photodegradable (Hemphill 1993). Unlike used greenhouse film, which is relatively clean and may have a recycling market established, field mulch and drip irrigation tape/tubing are dirty, making recycling less attractive. Incineration of these materials to retrieve their heat energy and use it to heat greenhouses or other buildings is a potential option for disposal that is being investigated by a team of researchers at The Pennsylvania State University. See chapter 12, "Managing Used Agricultural Plastics," for more information (page 116).

chor the plastic and drip tube by covering the end with soil and having a person stand on the drip tube. If this is not done, the drip tube will be pulled under the plastic mulch. As an alternative to purchasing machines for laying plastic mulch and drip tube and fumigating the soil, custom applicators are available.

For single-row crops, such as tomatoes, cucumbers, muskmelons, honeydews, watermelons, and pumpkins, the drip irrigation tube should be placed 4–5 inches from the center of the bed and 2–3 inches deep, with the emitter holes facing upward. For double-row crops, such as summer squash, okra, eggplant, sweet corn, and peppers, the drip tube should be placed directly on the center of the bed and buried 2–3 inches deep. A roll contains approximately 7,500 feet of drip tube, depending on the manufacturer. On 5-foot row centers, there are 8,712 linear feet of row per acre, so a grower would need about three and a half 2,400-foot rolls of plastic mulch and 1.2 rolls of drip tube per acre. On 6-foot centers, the per-acre requirements would be three rolls of plastic mulch and one roll of drip tube.

CHAPTER 3

Drip Irrigation and Water Management

David S. Ross

The production of quality produce requires adequate water to meet the daily water requirements of the crop. Severe water stress will reduce crop yield and can cause plant death. Irrigation systems are a necessary insurance for a successful production season.

Irrigation requires a reliable water supply. The quantity of water available may dictate the type of irrigation system that can be used. Overhead irrigation systems do not deliver water very well to plant roots under plastic mulch, but they are sometimes considered for frost protection, which requires a continuous low application rate over the entire crop at the same time. Overhead application has some disadvantages, however. Water washes pesticides off foliage, and moisture on foliage may encourage disease development. Evaporative losses during application can result in only 70–80% of the water reaching the root zone in windy, hot, dry weather. Overwatering results in water runoff and deep percolation beyond the root zone—other means of losing a valuable water resource.

Drip irrigation (also called trickle or microirrigation) is a popular method in many areas because of limited available water supplies; however, it is not limited to small-water-supply areas. These systems offer many advantages over overhead sprinkler systems. Drip systems deliver water to the crop row and the crop root zone rather than broadcast water over the entire land surface. This reduces the total water required and is more precise in placing water under plastic mulch. Drip systems operate at a lower pressure than overhead systems. Evaporative losses are less when compared to overhead, with 90–95% of the water reaching the root zone (if runoff is avoided).

Drip systems are the irrigation systems of choice in many areas because of their efficiency and compatibility with plastic mulch for rowcrops. Water management and irrigation scheduling are important for maximizing efficiency. Using sensors to monitor soil moisture and data to help manage the system is important to the overall success of the irrigation system.

Plant-Soil-Water Relationships

The true success of an irrigation system depends on proper design and management. Information about the water requirements of the crop being grown, knowledge of the water-holding capacity of the soil and the lateral movement of water, and an understanding of the water delivery rate of the irrigation system guide the irrigator to proper management decisions.

Plant Water Use

Plant water use is described by evapotranspiration (ET) during the vegetable cropping seasons in the United States. ET typically ranges from 0.10 to 0.25 inch per day in humid climates. For a few crops and in windy, arid climates, ET will peak at 0.35 to 0.45 inch per day. Corn will use up to 0.35 inch per day during tasseling if growing conditions are favorable.

Crop ET follows the diurnal flux of solar radiation, meaning 30–40% of the daily ET can occur during the two-hour period encompassing solar noon. This pattern of water use can result in short-term crop water stress if irrigations are not scheduled properly to provide sufficient soil water during this time.

Vegetable crops are in peak production with high crop water requirements during the months of high evaporative demand. Tomato, watermelon, and many other vegetable crops have high water-use rates.

Plant-Available Soil Moisture

Soils are able to hold a quantity of water based on their texture. Course-textured soils such as sands hold a small amount of water on their large soil particles. Fine-textured soils such as clays have many times as many small particles and, as a result, have much more surface area to hold water. Water is held to soil particles by a soil moisture (or surface) tension (SMT). Some of this water is held so tightly that plant roots are not able to remove it.

After a heavy rain or irrigation, the pore space between soil particles is filled with water. Gravity causes excess water to drain away, but the rest is held by the soil particles. Field capacity (FC) is a term describing the soil moisture when the soil particles are holding as much water as possible. Air needed by plant roots fills the rest of the soil pore space. Available water (AW) describes the amount of water that plant roots can extract from the soil. When plant roots can remove no more water, the soil is said to be at the permanent wilting point (PWP). The rest of the water is held tightly to soil particles. Figure 3-1 illustrates water and air content in a rain-gauge fashion for soil.

Many shallow-rooted crops are sensitive to even short-term water deficits and need to be watered when 33–50% of the available water is consumed. This easily extracted water is called usable water. A goal in irrigation scheduling is to maintain the usable water in the soil so plants always have a water supply available to them.

Available water ranges from 3 to 5% of total volume for sandy soils and up to 20% for very fine-textured soils. A soil water-holding capacity chart would show 5% moisture as 0.6 inch of water per foot of soil depth (0.05 times 12 inches per foot), and 20% moisture would be 2.4 inches of water per foot of soil depth. Table 3-1 illustrates the plant-available water-holding capacity ranges for a few different soil textures. Irrigation should begin when 50% of the available water is gone.

TABLE 3-1
Available water-holding capacity for different soil textures

SOIL TEXTURE	AVAILABLE WATER-HOLDING CAPACITY (inches of water per foot of soil)
Sand	0.25–1.00
Sandy loam	1.25–1.75
Clay loam	1.75–2.50
Clay	1.50–2.25

SOURCE: C. A. Storlie, 1995

Water Distribution under Drip

Water movement and distribution in the soil from drip emitters is influenced primarily by the texture of the soil (photo 3-1). In very sandy soils, water moves only 6–12 inches laterally from the emitter. In finer-textured silt and clay soils, the water will move 16–32 inches laterally from the emitter. Sandy soils will hold

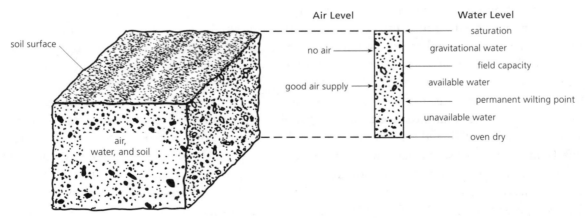

Figure 3-1. Soil at field capacity contains soil, air, and water in good balance for crop production. From field capacity to the permanent wilting point, plant-available water is gradually depleted and irrigation is necessary.

SOURCE: Ross, Maryland Cooperative Extension Bulletin 356, 1997.

Photo 3-1. Water movement and distribution in a sandy loam soil from a drip irrigation tape buried 2–3 inches deep and offset to the left side of the raised bed.

very little usable water, perhaps only 2% of the soil volume, compared with 10% for heavier, fine-textured soils. Water movement may change over the growing season, as the soil becomes more compacted.

A low continuous water application rate is best for achieving the lateral movement of the water. By using low-flow-rate emitters, higher oxygen content can be maintained in the wetted zone. For practical purposes, a new drip irrigation operator should set aside an area that can be dug up to check the water movement and the wetted volume of soil several times over the season. This experience will help in understanding the soil-water relationship on a particular farm.

If mulched raised beds are used for production, the crop roots will fill the raised bed soil volume by the end of the season. That soil volume will be the primary source of water for the crop, particularly for shallow-rooted vegetable crops. The drip tape will have to distribute water to that volume. In calculating soil volume, the width will be the width of the mulched bed, and the depth will be the rooting depth of the crop. Some crops will have a greater rooting depth than the depth of the raised bed.

After calculating soil volume, the next step is to estimate how much water the crop will need daily.

Calculations can be made to show that if the evapotranspiration rate is 0.20 inch per day for a maturing crop on 4-foot bed centers, then 50 gallons of water daily per 100 feet of row must be replaced in the soil. Design the irrigation system to supply all the crop water, if necessary, rather than just supplemental water.

Acre-inch of water (27,154 gallons) x 0.20 inch/day
= 5,430 gallons/day

There are 10,890 running feet of row
at 4-foot centers, therefore:

100 feet of row =
0.009% (of 10,890 feet) x 5,430 gallons
= 48.8 gallons/100 feet of row

If the operator is using a drip tape with 12-inch emitter spacing and the emitters discharge 0.30 gallon per hour (gph), then the tape is applying 30 gph per 100 feet (1 emitter per foot x 100 feet x 0.30 gph per emitter = 30 gph). In order to get the 50 gallons of water the crop used during the day, the system must operate 1.7 hours each day (50 gallons ÷ 30 gph). In this example, the tape is discharging 0.5 gallon per *minute* (gpm) per 100 feet, a common application rate.

A series of tables of data can simplify these calculations, but many factors are not easily taken into account, such as rainfall, stage of growth of the crop, weather, and water-holding capacity of the soil. Water management should not be based on a fixed daily operating time. Monitor soil moisture on a daily basis to help make irrigation scheduling decisions. The next section discusses tools and techniques to help determine soil moisture levels.

Water and Nutrient Management

Proper management of both water and nutrients is important for economic and environmental reasons. Resource management is critical, as water supplies are being depleted. Nutrients in water supplies are an environmental concern. When drought occurs, one never knows how long irrigation may have to serve as the major source of water for the crop. Water management is important from the beginning of the season to ensure that the water resource lasts as long as possible. Underwatering reduces crop growth and productivity. Overwatering not only moves excess water below the crop root zone by deep percolation but also moves nutrients along with that water. Overirrigation during any one application potentially leaches soluble plant nutrients such as nitrogen and potassium from the root zone, particularly on soils with low cation exchange capacity (CEC). On the other hand, when saline irrigation water sources are used, leaching may be necessary to remove harmful salt accumulations. For these reasons, it is important to put some data into the decision-making process using either a water budget bookkeeping method or a low-cost instrument for monitoring soil moisture.

Irrigation scheduling is a management duty that uses information about rainfall, crop water use, and soil water-holding capacity to plan the length of time that the irrigation system should be operated to replenish water used. The goal is to maintain a good soil moisture level without causing runoff or deep percolation (movement of the water below the roots into deeper soil where roots cannot retrieve the water).

One of the advantages of drip irrigation is that the system is always in the field and available for use. The goal of irrigation is to use frequent irrigations to maintain a uniform moisture level in the soil without causing saturation of the soil. The crop should not experience wilting at any time. Overwatering should be avoided. Feed the plant water, as it needs it.

Tools to Monitor Soil Moisture

One tool for monitoring soil water is a device called a tensiometer. A tensiometer measures the water tension, the attractive force that holds water onto soil particles. As shown in figure 3-2, a tensiometer consists of a water-filled tube with a porous ceramic tip on one end and a vacuum gauge on the other end. A water reservoir and cap (to seal the tube shut) are also on the gauge end. The porous tip of the tensiometer is placed into the plant root zone of the soil. As the soil dries out from plants extracting water, the soil pulls water from the water-filled tube with its attractive force. This water movement continues until the water tension force in the soil reaches equilibrium with the vacuum pulled on the gauge of the tensiometer. Now

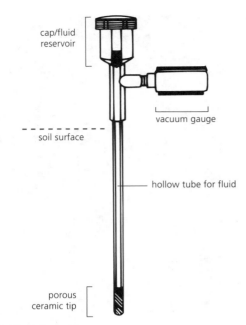

Figure 3-2. Typical tensiometer

the soil tension is read on the tensiometer gauge.

The vacuum gauge reads from 0 to 100 centibars (cb) (100 centibars = 1 bar = 1 atmospheric pressure = 15 pounds per square inch). Wet soils give low readings and dry soils give high readings. The tensiometer actually works best in sandy (coarse) soils but can be used in clay (fine) soils to show that the soils are moist. In clay soils, the moisture tension at which 50% of the available water has been consumed is just beyond the usable range of the tensiometer. The upper limit of tension that the tensiometer can read is about 80 cb, where the water column in the tube breaks and allows air to enter the device. After breaking tension, the device ceases to operate correctly until it is serviced. Thus, the tensiometer is more practical in coarse-textured soils than fine-textured soils.

Two pairs of tensiometers per management zone are suggested (photo 3-2). One pair should be placed in the droughtiest portion of the zone. This area of the field will need water sooner than other parts. The second pair should be placed in soil that is average for the site. A management zone can be several acres if the soil is reasonably uniform.

Recommended depths for tensiometer placement are a minimum of 6–9 inches of depth for one instrument and roughly 15–18 inches (about three-quar-

Photo 3-2. Pair of tensiometers in a staked tomato crop.

Table 3-2 (page 20) gives guidelines for using the tensiometer in different soils. As with any tool, expect to spend some extra time initially learning to use the tensiometer. Learn how the tensiometer reacts to soil moisture and how to base irrigation decisions on the tensiometer. Begin by reading the tensiometer every day at the same time, noticing how it climbs quicker on hot, dry days than it does on cool, cloudy days when plants use less moisture. Observe how young, small plants use less water than older, larger plants, which is evidenced by the tensiometer changing much more slowly in the early season. Record the daily tension readings on a graph. Place tensiometer readings on the vertical scale and days on the horizontal scale. Use 31-day graphs (moisture readings versus the day of the month) so the response can be reviewed later. Drops in the tension readings will indicate rainfall or irrigation events.

ters of the depth of the root zone) for a second one. Figure 3-3 illustrates the placement of two tensiometers relative to rooting depth and typical root density in the soil. Tensiometers are placed where the plant roots are actively growing. Placing the tensiometer in the zone of lateral water movement is best. This will ensure that the tensiometer senses the water when it moves out into the root zone. Place the device about 6–12 inches horizontally from the base of the plant and on the opposite side of the row from the drip line. The distance from the drip line depends on the soil texture. For sandy soils, it may be 8 inches to 1 foot. For a clay loam soil, it may be 1–2 feet. The tensiometer should not be in the saturated zone close to the drip line.

Servicing tensiometers after they are placed in the field is simple but important. Very little service is required unless a tensiometer breaks tension. This occurs when the soil is allowed to dry to tensions above 80 cb. When this happens, the tensiometer will either stay at 70–80 cb or drop to a deceptively low value. In either case, the tensiometer will no longer function properly. The only reliable way to know that tension has been broken is to look at the water column near the vacuum gauge. If there is a break in the water column, then service is required.

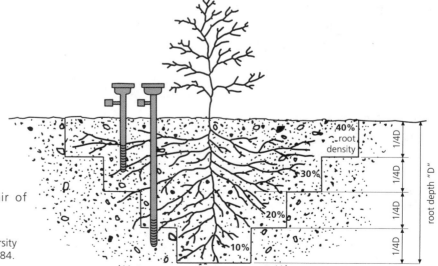

Figure 3-3. Placement of a pair of tensiometers in the crop root zone

Source: Ross and Brodie, Department of Biological Resources Engineering, University of Maryland, Publication FACTS 149, 1984.

TABLE 3-2
Soil tension guidelines for using tensiometers

SOIL MOISTURE and IRRIGATION STATUS	SOIL TEXTURE	SOIL TENSION (centibar)
Soil at field capacity— no irrigation required	Sand, loamy sand	5–10
	Sandy loam, loam, silt loam	10–20
	Clay loam, clay	20–40
50% of available water depleted— irrigation required	Sand, loamy sand	20–40
	Sandy loam, loam, silt loam	40–60
	Clay loam, clay	50–100

Source: C. A. Storlie, 1995

To service the tensiometer, open the cap and refill the water column. Gently tap the side of the reservoir, or insert a plastic drinking straw to break the water tension to allow water to flow into the tube. If the water level drops below the gauge opening, use the hand vacuum pump to remove any air that may be trapped in the gauge. Usually this will not be required. Reseal the tensiometer. Now it is ready for use again. It is not necessary to remove the tensiometer from the soil to service it. It is very important that the tensiometer tip maintain a firm contact with the soil.

At season's end, the tensiometers must be removed from the soil to prevent freezing and splitting. They should be drained, cleaned, and stored dry for the next season.

Gypsum blocks or their solid-state electronic replacements are recommended for medium to heavy soils such as clay loam and clay (fine texture) that hold 1.5 or more inches of available water per foot of soil (see table 3-1, page 16). They should be placed in the field similarly to tensiometers. These sensors are lower in cost than tensiometers, but a meter must be purchased to read them. The blocks are installed in the ground for each growing season, and a meter is attached to lead wires from the blocks to take the readings. Figure 3-4 shows the gypsum block installed in the soil using a piece of pipe and a meter connected to the lead wires from the block.

Daily readings and record keeping are the best way to learn how to use them. After experience is gained, daily readings may not be needed depending on the crop and soil conditions. Study the manufacturer's literature to learn specific instructions for use.

Water budget bookkeeping is another method of monitoring water status in the soil. The water-holding capacity of the soil can be obtained from a county soils book. After a good rainfall or irrigation event has filled the soil with water, start a daily record of rainfall amounts, irrigation amounts, and plant-use amounts. The initial amount of water entered into the record is that held in the root zone (1–2 feet of soil depth, depending on the crop). The bookkeeping method involves subtracting daily crop water use (0.15–0.25 inch) and adding amounts of water from irrigation or rainfall. A shallow pan (called an evapotranspiration pan) can be used to observe and measure the amount of water evaporated daily; this can be used for estimating crop water use.

The feel method involves taking a shovel and digging down into the root zone to grab a handful of soil to examine (table 3-3). This method is a manual method of learning how far irrigation water is going down into the soil to help the operator determine the

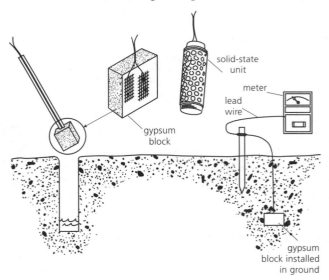

Figure 3-4. Gypsum block or its solid-state replacement
Source: Ross and Brodie, Department of Biological Resources Engineering, University of Maryland, Publication FACTS 149, 1984.

TABLE 3-3

Measuring soil moisture levels using the soil hand feel test

AVAILABLE MOISTURE IN SOIL	FEEL OR APPEARANCE OF SOIL			
	COARSE-TEXTURED SOILS (SAND); GRITTY WHEN MOIST, ALMOST LIKE BEACH SAND	MODERATELY COARSE-TEXTURED SOILS (SANDY LOAM); GRITTY WHEN MOIST, DIRTIES HAND; SOME SILT AND CLAY	MEDIUM-TEXTURED SOILS (SILT LOAM); STICKY WHEN WET	FINE- AND VERY FINE-TEXTURED SOILS (CLAY LOAMS AND CLAY); STICKY WHEN MOIST, BEHAVES LIKE CLAY
0–50%	Dry, loose, and single-grained; flows through fingers. Appears to be dry; does not form a ball under pressure.[1]	Dry and loose; flows through fingers. Appears to be dry; does not form a ball under pressure.[1]	Powdery dry; in some places slightly crusted but breaks down easily into powder. Somewhat crusty but holds together under pressure.[1]	Hard, baked, and cracked; has loose crumbs on the surface in some places. Somewhat pliable; forms a ball under pressure.[1]
50–75%	Appears to be dry; does not form a ball under pressure.	Forms a ball under pressure but seldom holds together.	Forms a ball under pressure; somewhat plastic; sticks slightly under pressure.	Forms a ball; ribbons out between thumb and forefinger.
75% to field capacity	Sticks together slightly; may form a very weak ball under pressure. Upon squeezing, no free water appears.	Forms weak ball that breaks easily; does not stick. Upon squeezing, no free water appears.	Forms ball, very pliable; sticks readily if relatively high in clay. Upon squeezing, no free water appears.	Ribbons out between fingers easily; has a slick feeling. Upon squeezing, no free water appears.
100% to field capacity	Same as above and upon squeezing, no free water appears on soil, but wet outline of ball is left on hand.	Same as above and upon squeezing, no free water appears on soil, but wet outline of ball is left on hand.	Same as above and upon squeezing, no free water appears on soil, but wet outline of ball is left on hand.	Same as above and upon squeezing, no free water appears on soil, but wet outline of ball is left on hand.
Above field capacity	Free water appears when soil is bounced on hand.	Free water is released with kneading.	Free water can be squeezed out.	Puddles, free water forms on surface.

Source: *National Engineering Handbook,* U.S. Department of Agriculture, Natural Resources Conservation Service.

Note: Depending on the stage of growth, irrigation method, and soil type, irrigation should be started when the soil is at 50–75% field capacity in the root zone. Soil moisture should not drop to less than 50% field capacity, or wilting can occur.
[1] A ball is formed by squeezing a handful of soil very firmly.

effects of a certain length of irrigation cycle. With experience, one can learn to differentiate between wet and dry soil. It requires considerable skill to judge field capacity and adequate usable water.

Newer methods of moisture sensing are available on the market, but most are still prohibitively expensive for the size of farm operations in the eastern United States. All irrigators are encouraged to try to monitor their soil water content to conserve both water and nutrients.

System Planning Considerations

Planning considerations include compiling full information about the water supply (both quantity and quality), crops to be grown, power sources, and topo-graphic and other physical characteristics of the farm and fields. The grower must make a long-range cropping plan so that the irrigation system can be designed to meet present and future needs. The first concern is finding out how much water is available to use. Then crop and farm information is needed to plan the irrigation system.

Water Source and Quality

A water supply is critical. Establishment of a water source comes first when considering an irrigation system. A good well is the first choice, because it is usually a clean supply of water. A drip system must have clean water, because the emitters that deliver the water are very small and clog easily when the water is dirty. A stream, spring, or pond can be used, but the water must be filtered more extensively to remove the particles in it (photo 3-3). Filtration is a requirement regardless of the water supply, but the more dirt particles or organic matter such as algae, the more important filtration is.

Most wells are very clean, but in some regions, fine sands are carried in the water. There is also the danger of dirt particles in the pipelines after installation or after a break in a pipeline. A filter at the field adds protection against clogging.

A surface water source must be evaluated for its flow under the worst conditions of the growing season. A procedure for estimating stream flow rate is given below. A well must be reliable in the middle of summer. It is wise to evaluate the source under the worst conditions and not to plan on more flow than is realistic.

The minimum quantity of water needed is roughly 30–50 gallons per minute per acre irrigated at one time. The specific amount depends on the row spacing of the crop and the application rate of the emitter system. For planning purposes, use the figures above to do the initial evaluation of the water source. Smaller or larger sources will allow more or less acreage to be irrigated at one time.

In some cases, intermediate water storage can be created to collect water from the primary source. Over a 24-hour time period, water is directed into the storage area, such as several tanks or a pond. A second pump is used to irrigate a small area of high-value crop using the stored water. The system must be designed to work within the restrictions of the water supply. Irrigating overnight from a small household well helps

ensure that water will be available for the household during the day.

Water quality may be an issue. A water test for irrigation purposes should be done using a qualified laboratory. This ensures that any potential problems with the water are known in advance. Physical treatment by filtration is a recommendation for all water sources and will be discussed later in more detail (see page 29). Chemical treatment may be needed to supplement filtration for some waters. The type of treatment needed depends on the situation and the specific water source.

Estimating stream flow rate is relatively easy. A few measurements and basic math are required. The process first determines the stream cross-sectional area and measures the average speed of the water flow. The volume of water per unit time flowing in the stream is then calculated as follows:

Pick a relatively uniform section of the stream, where width and depth are fairly constant for 10–15 feet or more. Avoid an area with debris or obstructions in the middle portion of the stream. At one point along the stream, measure and record the width of the stream. At equal intervals starting with zero depth at the bank, measure and record the stream depths across to the other bank. Calculate the average depth by adding together the depth measurements and dividing by the number of measurements, including the zeros. Multiply the average depth times the width to get the cross-sectional area. Calculate the area in square feet.

Determine water velocity. Place a chip or stick in the middle of the stream and let it float downstream. Measure the distance in feet between the starting and stopping points. Measure the time in seconds, if convenient, but try for one minute of time. Calculate the velocity in feet per minute. Water flows faster at the surface in the middle of the stream, so multiply the velocity by 0.7 to get an average stream velocity.

Determine the stream flow rate by multiplying the cross-sectional area by the average stream velocity to get cubic feet per minute. Convert the stream flow to gallons per minute by multiplying the cubic feet per minute by 7.5.

This process should be done two or three times to ensure a good estimation. The measurements should be made during the dry season to get the lowest seasonal flow rate. Do not make the estimate after a rainfall, when the flow is temporarily higher.

Photo 3-3. A farm pond can serve as a water source for drip irrigation.

A very small stream may be dammed up to force the water to flow through a pipe installed in the dam. A bucket and stopwatch can be used to measure the flow rate of the water from the pipe. Flow from a well pump can also be checked using this method.

An existing well and pump can be evaluated for flow rate using the following procedure. On the supply line coming from the pump, install a pressure gauge upstream from a gate valve. Direct the water into a bucket or tank large enough to catch 30 seconds or more of water flow. With the pump running, adjust the gate valve to establish 30 or 40 psi (pounds per square inch) pressure on the gauge. An irrigation system will require a minimum of 30 or 40 psi operating pressure at the pump. Use a stopwatch to time how long it takes to catch some number of gallons of water in the container. This method allows the flow rate at a specific pressure to be measured. This method does not evaluate the actual yield of the well, just the capacity of the pump.

Planning and Information Collection

After determining that there is sufficient water supply to allow irrigation, the next step is to plan the irriga-

tion system in cooperation with a competent dealer or engineer. The planning phase should include gathering topographic information about the farm and making a five-year cropping plan. The irrigation system will be a capital investment to be used for many years, so the design must meet present and future needs.

The physical layout of the farm, with distances and elevations, is needed. Aerial photographs may be available from local agencies like the Natural Resources Conservation Service. A scaled map is desired so that fields can be measured and the water supply, fields, electrical power, future expansion areas, and other details can be marked. A topographic map shows the elevation changes and slopes, which are necessary for planning the drip system layout and figuring pump pressure requirements.

A detailed sketch of individual fields showing measurements, crop row orientation, number of crop rows, length of rows, spacing between rows, slopes and elevation, and distances relative to details discussed above is very helpful when discussing the system plan with a designer. Figure 3-5 shows the start of a sketch of this information. Information on the soils and farm terrain will help the designer understand water-holding capacities, infiltration rates, drainage problems,

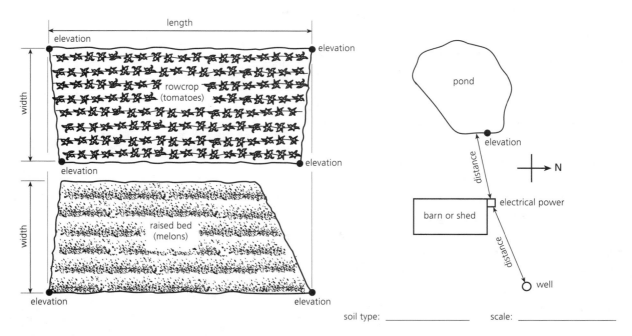

Figure 3-5. Field sketch shows planning information for irrigation system designer. Distances, elevations, field dimensions, crop spacing, utilities, water supply, and other pertinent information should be noted.

SOURCE: Ross, Maryland Cooperative Extension Bulletin 356, 1997.

and other factors. Details on the crops to be grown will help to define rooting depths and water requirements over the season.

Compile the details about the water supply and results of the water test for the designer. The water supply is one factor that will limit the design.

If there is an existing pump or well that is being considered for use, collect full information on the pump—horsepower; type (jet, submersible, centrifugal, or turbine); manufacturer; model and serial numbers; voltage; single- or three-phase; and any flow rate information. A pump chart will be needed to determine the flow and pressure capacities of the pump to evaluate its future use.

Laying Out the System

The word *design* is not used in this section because a competent, trained, experienced design person should make any design decisions for your system. There is not enough space here to cover all design considerations. However, having a preliminary plan is a good start.

The main control center is the first area to locate. It may be near the water supply, although that is not necessary. Components such as the pump, pump controls, fertilizer injector, primary filters, backflow prevention device, pressure gauges, and other items are located here. Electrical energy or a fuel-driven engine is necessary to operate the pump. All these components are semipermanent and can be housed in a shelter or building.

A mainline is laid out for underground installation to connect all the irrigation zones. PVC pipe can be trenched in, and then it is out of the way (photo 3-4). Riser pipes from the mainline will carry the water to the surface for distribution in the zone.

The mainline must be adequate to carry all available water, particularly if there are fields into which future expansion may be possible. It should also be large enough to maintain the water pressure. Adequate pressure at all the risers makes a system easier to manage. Water pressure is lost when water must travel at a high velocity through the pipe in order to get the required volume (gallons per minute) delivered. There is more friction of the water against the pipe walls at high velocity, and pressure energy is dissipated or lost. Pipe of a large enough diameter allows the water to

travel slower, resulting in reduced friction or pressure loss. Pressure will vary in the system due to elevation changes, but that is another matter.

The water supply must be matched to the irrigation zones—or actually vice versa. The irrigation system can deliver no more than the well, stream, or pump can supply. However, several irrigation zones can be created, to be watered one after the other. The discharge rate of the drip tape determines the length of tape and thus the feet of crop row in the irrigation zone. A low discharge rate means more feet of tape can be used for an irrigation zone, but it will take longer to water the given zone. There are tradeoffs in the process. A pump is used most efficiently when the irrigation water demand matches well with the pump discharge.

At the irrigation zone, a header or submain runs across the end of the field. At one end, the submain attaches to the riser pipe on the mainline. Along the submain and at the end of each crop row, a drip tape is attached. The submain supplies the water to the drip tapes, watering each crop row.

Between the riser pipe and the submain, there is a secondary control center (photo 3-5). This may be as simple as a manual valve to turn the water off and on to the irrigation zone. More often, an electrical solenoid valve and a pressure regulator are located here. A wire runs from the solenoid along the buried mainline back to the main control center to a controller that will operate the electric solenoid valve as required to water the zone. A secondary filter may also be located here.

Photo 3-4. PVC pipe trenched in, with riser pipes.

Photo 3-5. Secondary control center consisting of gate valve, pressure regulator, and screen filter.

There are considerations for emitter spacing, emitter discharge rate, length of run of the drip tape, placement of the drip tape on the contour or slightly downhill as opposed to uphill, and wall thickness of the tape. A dealer can recommend the tape product to use for the crop.

In a plasticulture system, the drip tape is laid along with the plastic mulch as the bed-forming machine crosses the field. The tape can be laid down separately.

It is laid off-center so that it will not interfere with the planting of the crop.

The biggest challenge comes in putting together the final system and finding the necessary fittings to make on the connections. Sizing the components properly makes for a good system.

System Components and Applications

A drip irrigation system has many important components that are selected to achieve a well-designed and functional system. A designer will pull all the information together to make the design. The user should have an understanding of all the components and their purposes. The major components of a drip system form the water-delivery system, including mainline distribution to the field, submain line within each irrigation zone, drip tape, filters, pressure regulators, gauges, and valves.

Information useful for design and selection of some components is included in this section. Figure 3-6 is an overall view of many of the components in a rowcrop drip irrigation system. Once the water supply and field layout information is known, the process of selecting and sizing components can begin.

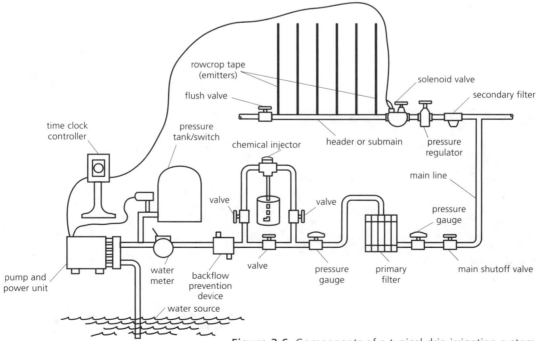

Figure 3-6. Components of a typical drip irrigation system for rowcrops
SOURCE: Ross, Maryland Cooperative Extension Bulletin 356, 1997.

Mainline Pipe

A temporary mainline of aluminum pipe laid aboveground can deliver the water to the field. A more permanent and out-of-the-way mainline is installed underground using polyethylene pipe in small applications or PVC pipe in larger systems. A properly sized buried mainline maintains the water pressure throughout the system and is out of the way for all aboveground operations. Riser pipes or hydrants are placed at each field or zone to provide the water.

Other components (to be discussed later) are attached to the riser to further distribute the water to the crop. These include pipe tees for multiple outlets, manual gate or ball valves, electric solenoid valves, pressure gauges, and pressure regulators. The submain or header pipe is attached to these components.

Submain or Header Pipe

The submain or header pipe is often a flexible or collapsible fabric or plastic pipe (sometimes called layflat) that lays across the end of each field on the surface to supply water to the lateral lines (drip tape) that run down each crop row or bed (photo 3-6). Tractors cross over the flexible header without damaging it during cultural and harvest operations. The header contains connectors at the proper interval for attaching the drip tape (laterals). The header can be reused for many years in fields with the same row spacing. It is removed, flushed, rolled up, and stored at the end of the growing season. In small systems, a polyethylene pipe may be used for the header. The polyethylene pipe is less flexible but resists punctures by rocky soil. In more permanent plantings, a buried PVC or polyethylene header with risers at each row may be used.

Lateral Connectors

Small plastic fittings are available for connecting the drip tape to the submain or header (photos 3-7, 3-8, and 3-9). Commercial connectors are designed for many different tape and pipe products. One early type of connector still in use is a small-diameter polyethylene tubing inserted into both the flexible layflat header and the drip tape through a punched hole in each component. The end of the drip tape is tied or folded and clamped to seal it shut. Barbed hose couplers have been used along with wire ties to connect pipe to tapes.

Drip or Lateral Lines

The lateral line in a vegetable, strawberry, or cut-flower crop is the drip tape that delivers the water to the crop.

Photo 3-6. Plastic pipe submain or header pipe in a field of potatoes grown on plastic mulch with drip irrigation.

Photos 3-7 and 3-8. Lateral connectors with an on/off valve in a plastic pipe header.

Photo 3-9. Lateral connectors in flexible layflat header.

In addition to the crop and soil considerations, the drip tape must be selected for the length of run (field lateral length) of the crop row, the slope of the lateral, and the amount of water to be carried. Tapes are available in many wall thicknesses, emitter spacings, and discharge rate combinations.

Drip Products. Drip lines are available in two product configurations, both of which are manufactured in various wall thicknesses, emitter spacings, and water discharge rates. Products are classed as tubes or tubing, which have attached or inserted emitters in heavier-walled material, and tapes, which have the emitters formed from the tubing material during the manufacturing process (photo 3-10). The drip tube is typically a heavier-walled polyethylene material that is flexible and does not collapse when not pressurized. It is used for long-term crops such as tree fruit and brambles. Drip tape is commonly used for vegetable, strawberry, and cut-flower crops.

Pressure-compensating emitters used on slopes or rolling terrain use inserted emitters in tubes or heavier tape. Pressure-compensating emitters are designed to regulate the water flow to a fairly constant discharge rate over a wide range of water pressures. Pressure regulation (discussed later) is important for achieving uniform water application. Irrigation zones laid out on the contour may use pressure regulators to control the pressure of water entering drip tape.

The tape products are made from a flat polyethylene sheet material into which the emitter is formed at regular intervals. Most of the tape products collapse flat when not pressurized and have wall thickness from

Photo 3-10. Roll of drip tape on plastic-laying machine.

4 mils (0.004 inch) for lightweight products to 20–25 mils for the heavyweight products. Vegetable, strawberry, and cut-flower production systems generally use drip tapes that are medium weight with wall thicknesses of 8–12 mils. A new user might use a thicker tape the first year or two while gaining experience.

Emitter spacing will affect the cost of tubes or tapes that have emitters inserted or attached. Conversely, emitter spacing has little effect on the cost of drip tapes with emitters molded into the tubing. A close emitter spacing of 8–12 inches is preferred in closely spaced (in-row) vegetable, strawberry, and cut-flower rowcrops (photo 3-11, page 28). Emitter spacings of 18–24 inches may be acceptable for use with crops that have greater plant spacing and on clay or loam soils. Rowcrops generally do best with line-source emitters; the discharge pattern is a continuously wetted volume of soil. Emitter spacing greater than 24 inches is rarely used, because water distribution and nutrient injection would be nonuniform.

Drip emitter discharge rates may be expressed in a couple different ways. The discharge rates of inserted or attached emitters are frequently expressed in gal-

Photo 3-11. Emitters spaced 12 inches apart are generally used for vegetables, strawberries, and cut flowers.

lons per hour (gph) for individual emitters, while the tapes with formed emitters are expressed in gallons per minute (gpm) flow per 100 feet of tape. The numbers are less confusing if the discharge rate is expressed in gallons per minute per 100 feet of length for a selected emitter spacing. Individual emitters commonly discharge between 0.15 gph to more than 1.0 gph under operating pressures of 6–15 pounds per square inch (psi) for tapes and 15–25 psi for tubes.

The emitters, particularly those that are not pressure-compensating, are influenced by the field slope, diameter of the tubing or tape, and length of run (length of tubing or tape in a lateral line). Typical lengths of run may range from 250 feet for high-flow, closely spaced emitters to 1,000 feet or more for low-flow emitters on greater spacing or for larger-diameter tubes or tapes. Products that are not pressure-compensating are generally limited to small slopes up to 3% to maintain uniform discharge along the length of the row. Larger-diameter tapes and tubes are being made to carry water for longer runs. Pressure changes due to elevation change or friction losses change the discharge rate along the length of the product. Water must move faster through longer-length tapes or tubes, and that results in more friction and pressure drop. The uniformity of application drops off as the lengths of run get longer.

A common tape selection for vegetable, strawberry, and cut-flower crops uses a 10-psi operating pressure with 0.30-gph emitters on a 12-inch spacing, which results in a rated tape discharge of 0.5 gpm (30 gph) per 100 feet of length. An emitter with a higher flow rate may discharge water too quickly on sandy soils to allow proper operation of a fertilizer injection system that needs a flush cycle after injection. Irrigation zones will be smaller, because the total length of tape in a zone will be less. A low-flow emitter extends the length of the irrigation cycle, which allows more time for injector operation and flushing. Irrigation zones can be larger. The small flow paths of low-flow emitters are susceptible to clogging and require more maintenance.

Field Water Requirements. Both the linear feet of drip tape per acre and the discharge rate dictate water requirements. Table 3-4 gives both the linear feet of product per acre for many bed spacings (center-to-center) and the gpm per acre for several product discharge rates. This table is helpful in planning for the use of small water sources and in determining the allowable zone size for larger water supplies.

For example, if a vegetable, strawberry, or cut-flower production field has beds on 5-foot centers and the chosen tape discharges 0.33 gpm (20 gph) per 100 feet, table 3-4 shows that 29 gpm per acre of water is required to operate the system. If a well produces only 30 gpm of water, then only 1 acre can be irrigated at one time. If the water supply is 300 gpm, then 300 gpm divided by 29 gpm per acre yields 10.3 acres as the maximum irrigation zone. Changing the tape to one with a discharge of 0.5 gpm per 100 feet, table 3-4 shows the water requirement to be 44 gpm per acre. The irrigation zone would be 300 gpm divided by 44 gpm per acre to equal 6.8 acres for the maximum area to be watered at one time.

Pump Capacity

Pump capacity is limited by the water supply but is selected to meet the irrigation zone requirements. Ideally, the irrigation zones will be matched or combined into equal requirements so the pump can operate at its most energy-efficient flow and pressure. Contrary to popular belief, the pump is not selected by horsepower. A pump is selected to provide the water flow rate required for the irrigation zones and the pressure head needed to make the whole system work. Pressure requirements include the energy to lift water from

TABLE 3-4

Conversion from bed spacing to linear feet of tubing per acre and to gallons per minute per acre for different tubing discharge rates (one line on each bed)

BED SPACING (center-to-center)			TAPE FLOW RATE, gph/100 feet[1]							
			15	20	25	30	35	40	50	75
			TAPE FLOW RATE, gpm/100 feet[1]							
INCHES	FEET	LINEAR FEET PER ACRE	0.25	0.33	0.42	0.50	0.58	0.67	0.83	1.25
			FIELD FLOW RATE, gpm/acre							
30	2.5	17,420	44	57	73	87	101	117	145	218
36	3	14,520	36	48	60	73	85	97	121	182
42	3.5	12,450	31	41	52	62	72	83	103	156
48	4	10,890	27	36	45	54	64	73	91	136
60	5	8,710	22	29	36	44	51	58	73	109
72	6	7,260	18	24	30	36	42	48	61	91

[1] Chart gives required water flow rate in gallons per minute (gpm) per acre. Heading is tape flow rate per 100 feet of length in both gallons per hour (gph) and gpm, because manufacturers use both units in descriptions.

a well or pond; pressure to push water up a hill to a field; friction loss in the pipes carrying the water plus that in filters, valves, and other components; and the operating pressure of the emitters. The pump is selected to provide the needed water flow rate at the required pressure head.

The type of pump depends on the amount of water required, the pressure required, location of the water, and the quality of the pump. Control devices to protect the pump should be considered. Centrifugal pumps work for surface water and shallow wells. Submersible pumps work in small- to moderate-yielding wells. Deep-well turbines or jet pumps are used in deeper wells. A pump dealer can advise on the specific situation.

An electrical motor, gasoline or diesel engine, or other power supply is then selected to power the pump. The selection takes into account the efficiencies of the power unit and power transmission to determine the horsepower required. Pump dealers have charts and tables to help make this selection.

Some growers replace overhead systems with drip and use the existing pumps. In most or all cases, both the flow rate and the pressure capacities of the exist-ing pump will be larger than needed for the drip system. The pump must be throttled back to a slower, less efficient speed. In this situation, some of the excess pressure can be used to operate a venturi-type fertilizer injection system.

Pressure tanks and pressure controls are used on small systems to maintain a pressurized system. The pressure control starts and stops the pump, similar to a household system. Electric time clocks and electric solenoid valves can operate the irrigation system. Water under pressure is available for other purposes. The pump does not have to be manually started and stopped.

Filtration

Filters are essential to the operation of a drip system and may be the most important component. Their function is to remove particulates from the water that would cause clogging of the emitters in the system. A primary filter is located near the water source to catch any incoming particles or precipitate from the fertilizer injection system. A secondary filter may be located in the field to catch any particles that enter the irrigation system through a pipe break or other means.

Filter selection is based on the type and amount of contaminants in the water, the maximum flow rate needed to operate the system, and the desired water quality. A complete water analysis for irrigation purposes will indicate the amount and type of contaminants and any chemical properties that may be problematic. Seasonal changes in the contaminant load should be considered in selecting and sizing filters.

Physical contaminants are suspended solids, such as organic and inorganic material. Organic refers to that which is or was living, such as algae, moss, worms, and plant material. Inorganic refers to sand, silt particles, and some chemical residuals in solid form. In addition to suspended solids, there are chemicals and minerals in solution. If these materials are maintained in solution, they will not cause clogging. When fertilizers or other chemicals are injected into water, chemical reactions may occur and cause precipitation of solids. Soluble iron or bicarbonates in the water supply may also react and precipitate out as solids under certain conditions.

Intake screens are used on the pump suction pipe pulling water from surface water sources to prefilter the water. These screens help to keep debris from damaging the pump and reduce the debris that reaches the main filters. Some intake screens are equipped with self-cleaning or flushing devices to remove algae and other organic matter that would clog the screen.

Four basic types of filters used in agriculture are the screen, disc, media or sand, and separator. For wells, municipal water, and relatively clean water supplies, a screen or disc filter can be used. Screen filters with 140- to 200-mesh screen sizes are available in a wide range of sizes matched to the flow rate of the system (photo 3-12). Some of these filters come with a flush valve that can be opened to force water to reverse its flow path and clean the debris out of the screen. Automatic flushing systems are available for larger screen filters. Disc filters have a stack of flat grooved discs that can capture more dirt than a screen filter (photo 3-13). The discs separate during cleaning to allow the particles to be flushed away. Although more expensive, they have more capacity to hold particles and are reliable and easy to clean.

Sand or media filters are absolutely necessary with any open or surface water (photo 3-14). Sand filters contain a sand filter bed. Water is distributed over the top of the sand and goes down through the sand. Any debris is trapped in the sand, and the clean water comes out the bottom. The filter bed acts as a maze and is effective in capturing organic and inorganic particles. Cleaning or backwashing the sand filter is done by taking clean water from one filter and running it in reverse direction through the filter to be cleaned. The water separates and lifts the sand to release the debris and flush it out a backwash port. The flow out of this valve is regulated so the backwash process does not carry the sand out. A minimum of two tanks is required for the backwash process. A pressure drop caused by clogging restricts water flow and signals a backwash or flush of the filter. Automatic controls set for a specific pressure drop will backwash a filter. Pressure gauges on both sides of the filter allow the operator to monitor clogging of the filter.

Photo 3-12. Screen filters are available in a wide range of sizes matched to the flow rate of the system.

Photo 3-13. Large disc filtering unit containing multiple disc filters.

Photo 3-14. Large 4-foot-diameter sand media filter.

Photo 3-15. Pressure gauge for a small system showing 7–8 pounds of pressure.

When figuring the water requirements for a system, part of the available water capacity is assigned for use in the backwashing function that may occur during the irrigation. Failure to include the additional water will cause the pressure to drop in the system, because there is an added discharge point. The lower pressure means the filter will not be cleaned properly.

The size of the filter and choice of media depends on the quantity and quality of water available and desired. The cleaner the water going into a filter, the cleaner it will be coming out. A dealer can advise on filter selection. The finest filtration comes with number 20 crushed silica, which gives 74-micron filtration that is equivalent to a 200-mesh screen. If a filter loads up quickly during parts of the season, a prefilter, chemical treatment, or added filter capacity may be necessary. Gravity screen filters with pressure-washing sprays may be used in ponds or moving water to separate intake water from larger debris. Gravity sand or gravel beds may also be used as prefilters.

Separators use centrifugal action caused by the water flow through the unit to cause particles of sand, silt, and other fine material greater than 325 mesh (44 microns) and heavier than water (by specific gravity) to fall out of the water flow. These units are often installed on wells as primary filters to remove sand and well mud before the secondary filter. This increases the operating time of the secondary filter between backwashes.

Pressure Gauges

Pressure gauges are the main management tool for monitoring system operation (photo 3-15). Accurate pressure is essential to proper performance of the irrigation system. A gauge allows the operator to see how much pressure is present at any location.

Pressure gauges are most useful at the pump, on either side of the filter, and in the irrigation zones. These locations allow the operator to make spot checks of system operation as rounds are made in the fields. High-quality gauges are filled with a liquid to dampen shock waves. Small valves can be used to isolate the gauge from the system except when the pressure is being checked.

Pressure Regulators

Establish the operating pressure of each zone with pressure regulators. The pressure in the mainline will vary over its length with elevation changes and the changing pressure losses of the filter and valve settings. It is better to have a higher pressure in the mainline and then use a pressure regulator to provide the correct pressure in the individual zones. Many drip tapes are designed to operate at 8 psi pressure. A pressure regulator has a spring-type or diaphragm-type regulator that maintains the water pressure beyond it at a set point. The mainline may be 20 psi or higher, but the header can be regulated to keep an average 8 psi in the drip tapes (laterals). There will be some friction loss, so the pressures will vary a little in the zone. But the pressure is held steady going into the zones.

Pressure regulators are inexpensive and reliable. Both adjustable and preset types (set to a certain pressure) are available. They are sized to the range of water flow through the device. They may not always be the same diameter as the water pipe to which they are attached, so pipe fittings may be needed to attach different size components. Select each component for the water flow rate it must carry.

Valves

Any number of different valves may be used in a watering system for different purposes. The simplest valves are manual gate or ball valves used to open or close supply lines to irrigation zones. Gate valves have a gate that slides open and closed to fully open or close the pipeline. A ball valve has an internal ball with a hole through it; aligning the hole with the pipeline opens the valve to permit water flow. These two types of valves have little restriction to flow when open. Partially-closing the valves will restrict flow and reduce the water pressure beyond the valve, but a pressure regulator is more appropriate.

Electric solenoid valves can be used to automate the system. With these valves, an electric current activates an electromagnetic switch that controls water flow by opening or closing the valve. A controller or simple time clock can operate the solenoid valve on a schedule to water the crop automatically. A water sensor or computer controller may also operate the solenoid valve remotely.

Air and vacuum-relief valves are located near pumps and throughout the system. These valves release accumulated air from pipelines and prevent vacuums from forming that might collapse the pipe. There are two basic types: noncontinuous-acting valves and continuous-acting valves. Noncontinuous-acting relief valves release air while the pipeline is being pressurized and are nonfunctional thereafter. They usually have a ball inside that rises to seal the valve closed when water fills the valve. They are placed at high points in the system. When the system is turned off and water drains out through the emitters, air can reenter the pipeline through the valve to reduce the chance of dirt being pulled in through the emitters. The continuous-acting valves are placed near pumps that pump air with the water. The valve opens even under pressurized conditions to bleed off trapped air. Pockets of trapped air can restrict water flow or cause water hammer. During water velocity changes, compressible trapped air can cause water to bounce off an air pocket and travel through the pipeline with dangerous force that can damage the pipe.

Check valves are one-way valves that allow water to flow only in one direction. An internal flap drops down to close the valve if water begins to flow in the opposite direction. These are used to protect pumps from water in the pipeline flowing backwards through the pump. They also protect the water source from contamination from chemicals injected into the irrigation water and prevent water from flowing into the chemical tank during a power failure.

Pressure-relief valves are spring-loaded valves that open to the atmosphere when the system pressure exceeds a set point. They let the water blow off until the pressure drops to a safe level. These valves are used to protect the pipeline against damaging high pressure.

Controllers

While manual valves can be used to turn the water flow on and off, a controller is an electrical time clock device that can be programmed to automatically operate electric solenoid valves. Irrigation can be controlled by programming the length of time each solenoid valve is open to allow water to enter a specific zone. The soil moisture condition is first determined, and then the timer is programmed. The controller waters one zone after another until everything is watered. Different controllers have different features that allow other options. The controller saves labor, because a person can do other tasks rather than watching the time and changing manual valves.

Backflow Prevention Devices

A backflow preventer is a safety device to stop the backflow of water or chemicals from an irrigation system into a potable water source. On a farm, backflow prevention is used with fertilizer injection systems, with irrigation wells, and on home hose bibs. The water source or a chemical supply may be protected from the flow of water to it. Backflow prevention devices have several designs based on the degree of protection to be provided. For a farm system, a check valve provides minimum backflow protection. A better backflow preventer has a check valve, air/vacuum breaker valve, and a low-pressure drain inside a single unit or as separate components. The goal is for no water to flow back past the check valve into the source. The vacuum-relief valve prevents a vacuum from occurring that could cause leakage around the check valve. The low-pressure drain will open to drain any leakage off to a safe place.

Chemical Injection Equipment

Several types of chemical injection systems are available for farm use. Liquid and soluble fertilizers, liquid chlorine, and acid are commonly injected. During the system planning stage, it is a good idea to prepare for an injection system whether it will be installed immediately or at a later date. It is best to install the injection system on a parallel bypass on the irrigation system. A parallel bypass means the irrigation system splits into two parallel paths and then rejoins into one path. The injector can be installed on one side of the bypass. Irrigation water can bypass the injector by flowing on the other path. Valves on both paths allow the flow of water to be controlled to either path, as appropriate. If an injector is not in the initial plans, install and cap two tees on either side of a gate valve in the irrigation line after the pump for later completion of the bypass.

A venturi-type injector is low-cost and easy to install on a parallel bypass in the system after the pump (photos 3-16 and 3-17). A venturi device works on a pressure differential principle, meaning that a large pressure drop through the venturi causes a suction within a constricted throat that pulls in the fertilizer solution. The large pressure differential must be created by the irrigation pump, meaning a lot of energy is used by the main pump to inject fertilizer, or a small booster pump is installed on the bypass with the injector to create the extra pressure on a small water flow. In the first case, a valve throttles the flow on the irrigation side of the bypass causing a lot of pressure (energy) to be consumed pushing water through the restriction. When a pump formerly used for overhead irrigation is used for drip irrigation, there is extra pressure capacity available that can be used for this purpose. If the irrigation pump will be expected to operate a venturi injector, increase the pump's pressure capacity when it is selected. Pressure fluctuations in the system will make the rate of injection difficult to control.

Water-powered injector pumps use a little of the energy in the irrigation water to run a piston pump

Photo 3-16. Small venturi system for injecting fertilizer.

Photo 3-17. Venturi system for injecting fertilizer prior to the sand media filters.

that is directly connected to an injector piston pump (photo 3-18, page 34). The energy consumption is low, and the injection is directly proportional to the water flow. The application is uniform at a known rate. Adjustments can be easily made.

Electric motor– or gasoline/diesel engine–driven injection pumps are also available. They power piston, diaphragm, roller, or pinch pumps. They provide a constant injection rate and may not be accurate in systems where water flow rates vary in different zones.

A bladder tank or proportioning tank injects liquid fairly uniformly. A collapsible bag inside a tank contains the fertilizer solution. Irrigation water is allowed to flow into the tank around the bag to cause the bag to collapse. As the bag collapses, the liquid flows through a control valve into the irrigation system downstream. These injectors are used in greenhouses where small amounts of liquid are injected.

Photo 3-18. Water-powered Dosatron injector pump.

They are limited by their volume in the amount of liquid injected and must be recharged in batches.

System Installation, Operation, and Maintenance

Careful planning will make the installation, operation, and maintenance of the drip system much easier.

Installation

Permanent installation of underground PVC mainlines keeps them out of the way and out of sight. Place pipe risers at a convenient spacing in the field for future connections if specific zones have not been finalized. Electric wires for controllers or for solenoid valves can be buried with the pipe. A control center with the pump, water filters, fertilizer injector, pressure gauges, and other components can be in a permanent shelter or built onto portable platforms to move at the end of the season. The drip tape can be installed by several mechanical methods. The drip lines and plastic mulch can be installed in one operation. Drip lines may also be installed a few inches deep in the ground or onto bare ground by other equipment. Fittings are available to easily connect the drip laterals onto a flexible header or submain. A section of pipe containing a valve and pressure regulator connects the submain to the mainline.

Operation

The initial operation of a new drip irrigation system is a learning experience. As suggested earlier, new users should set aside a section of the system where the soil can be excavated to observe the moisture pattern. Use tensiometers (or other sensors) and observe how they respond. Watch the daily tensiometer readings and set the irrigation schedule to replace soil moisture. Try to avoid under- and overirrigation. Watch the system pressures and adjust them as needed. Check the filters frequently to see if there is much debris in the water, and clean them as necessary. Pressure gauges before and after the filter show the pressure loss as clogging occurs. Watch for system leaks and for damage by rodents and other animals.

Maintenance

Various maintenance duties may be needed for system upkeep. Maintaining water quality can be a big issue in some situations. Identify problems during the daily operation and attend to them quickly. Clean filters and monitor the system pressure.

Chlorination. Organic material, particularly algae, can cause trouble in a drip system by clogging the emitters. Chlorine injection is commonly used to eliminate algae, which is present in most surface water and in some well water. Chlorine acts as a powerful oxidizing agent in water and vigorously attacks organic materials.

Algae can work its way into the irrigation system through the smallest mesh filters. If it receives sunlight and water, it will begin to grow and will clog a drip system in a short time. The amount of chlorine required is based on water pH, water flow rate, and amount of algae present. Chlorine contact time in the system is important to achieve success.

To be effective, a residual of 1–2 parts per million (ppm) of active chlorine should be measurable at the end of the irrigation lines. The amount to add at the beginning of the system is determined by trial and error. The amount of algae present in surface water will vary over the season. The dosage will likewise vary over the season. A swimming pool chlorine test kit can be used to measure active chlorine. Household bleach contains 5.25% sodium hypochlorite; 2.6 fluid ounces of bleach per 1,000 gallons of water yields approximately 1 ppm chlorine. Chlorine levels over 100 ppm may cause injury or kill plants. Generally, 30–60 minutes of chlorination every 4–6 hours of irrigation works under normal conditions. High levels of chlorine may be used to clean a pipeline by filling the water pipe and letting it sit for 24 hours. Inject near the end of the irrigation cycle, unless continuous injection is required, and allow the active chlorine to stay in the pipe.

Water pH is important when using chlorine. It takes nearly twice as much chlorine to do the job when the pH is 7.5 or above than when the pH is somewhat less than 7.5. Acid treatment may be justified to lower the pH in some situations.

Chlorine is available in liquid, dry, and gaseous forms. Common household bleach may be used for small systems. For large systems, the gaseous form is used. Dry forms of chlorine are dangerous, because gas is released when the material becomes wet. The injection system used with chlorine gas has safety factors built into it to prevent gas from escaping. Chlorine gas is the least expensive form.

Chlorine is also used to oxidize soluble ferrous iron and to kill sulfur bacteria. For treatment of iron, use 1 ppm of chlorine for every 1 ppm of iron. The chlorine oxidizes and precipitates ferrous iron as well as kills iron bacteria present. Iron bacteria act on iron to form slime that clogs the emitter holes. For treatment of sulfur, 9 ppm of chlorine is needed for every 1 ppm of sulfur in the water. Sulfur bacteria are a problem. Use the same treatment as for algae on these bacteria.

Acidification. Acid may be necessary to lower the pH in order to halt precipitation of calcium carbonate, calcium phosphatic compounds, or iron oxides—all of which can plug drip emitters. A water test is needed to identify and quantify the problem. A reliable chemical dealer should recommend the amount and type of acid to use. CAUTION: Concentrated acids must always be added to water, never the reverse.

Muriatic acid (hydrochloric acid) or sulfuric acid is used to lower pH. They are easier to use than phosphoric acid. The water should always be tested if phosphoric acid is used in the drip system. Phosphoric acid, unless injected in the exact amount needed, will precipitate almost everything present in the water and cause clogging in the drip lines.

PVC and layflat hose should be cleaned and flushed every year before use. One-half gallon of 68.6% muriatic acid per 3-acre block will clean out mains and submains. Cleaning and flushing removes coatings of oil from the pump and the protective coating on fertilizer. Flakes of this material will fall off and clog drip lines.

Summary

Drip irrigation works well with plastic mulch in a very efficient production system that holds moisture in place for the crop and provides other benefits. Water and nutrients can be placed into the crop root zone very efficiently with little loss. Filtration is an essential part of the success of the system. Small water sources can be used to advantage. Crop productivity and crop quality benefit from drip irrigation. Water and nutrient management is a key to the successful use of irrigation.

CHAPTER 4

Fertigation

George J. Hochmuth, James W. Paterson, and Stephen A. Garrison

Microirrigation and fertigation refer to applying irrigation water and fertilizer nutrients through small emitters placed on or in the soil near the plants. Drip or trickle irrigation is a type of microirrigation where water and nutrients are dispensed to the crop via small plastic tubes with drip-type emitters that are placed near a row of plants. Drip irrigation is an important irrigation method in many crop-production areas of the world, particularly in areas where there is much competition for available water resources.

Drip irrigation has many benefits, some of which are becoming more important in today's environmentally conscious world. One of the major benefits of drip irrigation is the capability to conserve water and fertilizer. Research has shown that water savings with drip irrigation can amount to as much as 80% when compared to subirrigation and 50% when compared to overhead sprinkler irrigation (Locascio et al. 1981b, Elmstrom et al. 1981, Locascio et al. 1985). This benefit is extremely important for vegetable producers in urbanizing areas of the country.

Drip irrigation allows the precise timing and application of fertilizer nutrients in vegetable production. Fertilizer can be prescription-applied during the season in amounts that the crop needs and at particular times when nutrients are most needed. This capability helps growers increase the efficiency of fertilizer needs and should result in reduced fertilizer applications. The improved fertilizer application efficiency results from small, controlled amounts of fertilizers that are applied throughout the season, in contrast to the conventional practice of applying large amounts of fertilizer within or on the bed under the plastic mulch at the beginning of the season (Locascio and Smajstrla 1989, Locascio et al. 1989, Dangler and Locascio 1990a,b). Increased efficiency not only saves production costs but also reduces the potential for groundwater pollution due to fertilizer leaching after heavy storms or periods of excess irrigation.

Placing small amounts of fertilizer in the production bed when the crop requires them results in reduced potential for soluble salt injury to crops. This benefit of drip irrigation can improve plant stands and overall crop uniformity and yield and is particularly important when using water sources that are high in soluble salts (greater than 1,500 parts per million). Extra salt levels imposed on the production system by high levels of dry fertilizer in the bed can be reduced if the bulk of the fertilizer is applied in small amounts through the drip irrigation system.

Substantial acreage of vegetable crops, strawberries, and cut flowers are presently being grown in the Northeast using plastic mulches and microirrigation watering systems to enhance crop production while practicing environmentally sound farming operations.

System Design Considerations

The importance of proper design of a drip irrigation system for efficient operation cannot be overemphasized. Benefits are quickly lost in poorly designed systems. Growers should carefully investigate companies with whom they will contract for the system installation. These companies should have experience and an understanding of drip irrigation systems. They should be able to design a system to suit the particular needs of a specific production system. It is beyond the scope of this publication to discuss the specifics of complete drip irrigation design and installation. More detail is contained in chapter 3. For additional resources, see the references section on page 135.

Fertilizer Injectors

One important component of the drip irrigation system that is to be used for fertilizer management is the fertilizer injector (photo 4-1). Several types of injection systems are available; the major types include positive displacement (hydraulic or electric-powered) pump injectors, pressure differential systems, and venturi injectors. The choice of a particular injector depends on the desired longevity of the piece of equipment, the required accuracy of injection, the required injection rate, and whether or not corrosive chemicals such as acids will be injected into the drip irrigation system.

Photo 4-1. Fertilizer injection unit, screen filter, pressure regulator, and pressure gauge.

Backflow Prevention

Most states, by law, require that irrigation systems that will be injecting fertilizers have proper backflow and antisiphon equipment installed in the system. A backflow prevention system is needed to prevent the movement of water containing fertilizer or other injected chemicals back into the well or water source when the system is not operating. Antisiphon equipment is also needed to prevent the movement or suction of the fertilizer stock solution back into the irrigation lines when the system is not operating. Chapter 3 contains more information on backflow prevention systems. Local county Cooperative Extension offices can provide information as well.

Filtration

Another important component for all irrigation systems is filtration (Haman et al. 1986, Haman et al. 1988a, Haman et al. 1988b). Filtration requirements differ depending on the quality and source of the water supply (well water or surface water) being used for irrigation purposes. In most well-water systems, screen or disk filters are used to remove particulate matter such as sand or limestone brought in from the well (photo 4-1). For surface water systems, sand media filters may be used to trap particulate matter such as algae, bacteria, larvae, and organic matter that would be pumped into the irrigation system from the pond or lake. In systems where fertilizers are injected, it is usually necessary to add a secondary filtration step after the fertilizers are injected. The second filter will remove any particulate matter or precipitates that occur as the fertilizer materials are injected into the system. Filtration is extremely important in drip irrigation systems to prevent plugging and clogging of the small drip irrigation emitters and to maintain design levels of uniformity in water and fertilizer application to the crop. However, growers should consult with the particular irrigation tubing manufacturer to determine recommendations for exact filtration mesh requirements.

Emitters

Emitters in drip irrigation tubing systems vary among manufacturers. Some emitters are laser-cut openings or orifices at specified intervals along the tubing. Other types of emitters involve mechanisms that provide a tortuous pathway through which the water must pass before it is finally emitted into the soil. Generally, emitter discharge increases with system pressure. However, some types of emitters are pressure-compensating so that water discharge does not vary with variations in pressure.

The flow rate also is important in the overall design and management of the drip irrigation system. Most drip irrigation tubing discharge rates vary from 0.3 gallon per minute (gpm) per 100 feet of length to 0.6 gpm per 100 feet. Emitters with larger flow rates result in shorter durations of water application to achieve wetting of the root zone but are less prone to clogging. In some systems, high-flow-rate injectors are needed to achieve the desired amount of injected fertilizer within the run time constraints of the irrigation system. Therefore, it is important to consider the flow rate of the drip irrigation tubing in the overall design of the drip irrigation and fertilizer injecting components of the system.

Emitter spacing in the laterals in the field depends on the type of soil and type of crop being produced. Closer emitter spacing results in the potential for better distribution of water in the soil. Emitters that are spaced at wide distances (such as greater than 24 inches), especially on sandy soils, can result in dry spaces in the bed, particularly when one emitter becomes clogged. Emitter spacings on the order of 8–12 inches are optimum for closely spaced crops such as peppers, strawberries, squash, cucumbers, muskmelons, and cole crops. Emitter spacings may be expanded to 18 inches for wider-spaced crops such as tomatoes, watermelons, pumpkins, winter squash, and eggplant. The emitter spacing is also important in multicropping situations, where it would probably be better to choose tubing with relatively close emitter spacings, on the order of 12 inches, so that the drip tubing is suitable for nearly all multicrop possibilities.

Uniformity

The benefits achieved from drip irrigation depend to a large extent on the system maintaining its high degree of uniformity throughout the season. Uniformity can change if there are problems or failures in the components of the system, such as faulty pressure regulators or clogged drippers. Thus, periodic checks on emitter uniformity are required. Uniformity of fertilizer application can be no higher than the uniformity of water application.

Uniformity of application is tested by measuring the flow from various emitters in the field and calculating an efficiency value. Information on system design and field testing for uniformity is described elsewhere (Smajstrla 1981, Smajstrla et al. 1983b, Smajstrla et al. 1990). A simple field procedure described by Smajstrla et al. (1983b) is highly recommended for systems used for fertilizer application. Application uniformities greater than 90% are desirable for proper application.

THE EFFECTIVE WETTED ROOT ZONE

Efficiency of irrigation with drip irrigation is only realized if the water and fertilizer delivered by the system are confined to the plant root zone (Persaud et al. 1976, Persaud et al. 1977, Graetz et al. 1978, Sweeney et al. 1987). Management of the drip irrigation system should be such that water and fertilizers do not move below the root system of the crop. Research has shown that for tomatoes, more than 80% of the roots can be contained in the upper 12 inches of soil in a subirrigated field. When drip irrigation is used in fields that were traditionally subirrigated, the root zone might extend deeper than 12 inches. Growers will need to determine the root zone for their particular soil and crop. This knowledge will be critical to efficient management of water and nutrients.

Preplant Fertilizer

Liming

Most soil in the northeastern United States is naturally acidic, and many cultural practices used in farming operations tend to make the soil more acidic. Once the plastic mulch and drip irrigation systems are applied to soils with low pH, there is no effective way to lime and correct the acidity until after the crop and mulch are removed from the field. The longer the soil remains in an acidic condition and is continually farmed, the more detrimental an effect the soil acidity has on crop production. **Therefore, before beginning any cropping program, the producer should have the soil tested and correct the soil acidity.**

Following recommended liming practices will reduce soil acidity (increase soil pH) to a desirable level as well as supply the soil with needed calcium (Ca) and magnesium (Mg). When needed, lime should be applied as far ahead of the application of the plastic mulch and drip irrigation system as practical.

Starter Fertilizer

Current recommendations call for a small amount of fertilizer, either liquid or dry, to be applied in the bed as a starter fertilizer for drip-irrigated crops. This starter fertilizer should contain all of the phosphorus (P) and micronutrients and up to 40% of the nitrogen (N) and potassium (K). On soils testing very low in P and K, the starter can be broadcast or banded in the bed. If only small amounts of P and micronutrients are required, then it would probably be better to band these materials 2–3 inches below the bed surface and to the side of the plant row, but not between the drip tube and row. In most cropping situations, approximately 30–40 pounds per acre of N and K would be sufficient in the starter fertilizer mixture. The amounts of P and micronutrients should be determined by a calibrated soil test. In situations where the soil test index for P is high or very high, no P would be added to the soil.

Phosphorus and Micronutrients

In general, P and micronutrients are not recommended for application simultaneously in drip irrigation systems. This is because of precipitation events that can happen with the P and micronutrients or with the P and the Ca or Mg in the well water. Research has shown, however, that P can be successfully applied through drip irrigation systems with certain precautions (Rolston et al. 1981, Mikkelsen 1989). If application of P is required during the season (such as during cold periods), it should be injected as phosphoric acid alone, in a separate application event. Acidification of the irrigation water to pH 4.0–5.0 might be needed to keep the P in solution during the application. Acidification can be achieved by using phosphoric, sulfuric, hydrochloric, or other acids to reduce the pH of the water. Injection of P is possible and can be an efficient method of P application; however, injection must be done carefully with attention to water pH. CAUTION: Concentrated acids must always be added to water, never the reverse.

Micronutrient injection can involve some of the same problems encountered with P injection. The key is to avoid precipitation. If micronutrients must be injected, then soluble forms such as chelates, which are less subject to precipitation, should be used. Like P, micronutrients should be injected alone.

Although there are serious problems and considerations with injecting P and micronutrients, there are also several potential benefits from a properly conducted injection. Phosphorus and most micronutrients are immobile in the soil, so generally only one or two applications are needed. Research has shown that plant recovery of these nutrients can be increased when they are applied through the drip system (Rolston et al. 1981, Mikkelsen 1989). This is probably due to the resulting "bandlike" application by drip irrigation, where the nutrients are not widely mixed with the soil (in which case fixation would occur). Although only small portions of the root zone are exposed to the nutrients, research shows that not all of the root system needs to absorb the nutrient to benefit the plant.

Fertilizer Injection

Rates

In most situations, injected fertilizers will consist only of N and K. The amount of N to use is basically determined by the nutrient requirement for N for a particular crop. Amounts of N are recommended for each crop for each season. Recommendations are under continual revision as more research results become available.

The K amount to be injected is based on the soil-test-predicted amount of K required for the crop minus the amount of that soil-test-predicted K that is applied in the bed as a starter. For example, if the soil tested medium in K, perhaps only 100 pounds per acre K fertilizer would be required for the season. If 20% of this K (20 pounds) were applied in the bed as starter fertilizer, then 80 pounds would be injected through the season.

Sources

Several sources of N and K can be used for drip irrigation injection (Locascio et al. 1978, Locascio and Fiskell 1979, Locascio et al. 1981a, Locascio et al. 1982, Fiskell and Locascio 1983, Locascio et al. 1984, Locascio and Martin 1985). All sources must be highly water soluble to be effective for drip irrigation injection. Nitrogen sources including ammonium nitrate, calcium nitrate, various nitrogen solutions, and potassium nitrate can be used to supply the N.

Potassium can come from potassium nitrate, potassium chloride, or potassium sulfate.

Application Frequencies and Methods

It is most convenient to think of rates of injection in terms of pounds of a particular nutrient per acre per day or week. For example, the recommended rate of N injection for a particular crop might be to start out early in the season with 1 pound per acre per day, then increase to 1.5 pounds per acre per day, and finally inject 2 pounds per acre per day when the crop is at its peak growth rate.

Nutrients can be injected into the system in various frequencies. Basically, the frequency to inject, whether once a day or once every two days or even once a week, depends on system design constraints, soil type, and grower preference. Research has shown that the frequency, even up to once per week, is not as important as achieving a correct rate of application of nutrients to the crop during a specified period of time (Locascio and Smajstrla 1989).

Some growers find that computer control of drip irrigation systems makes it easy to inject more frequently, such as once every day. There would seem to be a slight advantage to this logistically. For example, injecting fertilizer more frequently, such as once per day, would reduce the chances that nutrients are leached from the beds due to a heavy rain storm or excessive irrigation compared to injecting larger amounts on a less frequent basis. If the chances for leaching losses are extremely low for any particular field, then injection once per week would be satisfactory. In any event, it is extremely important that the nutrients applied in any irrigation event are not subject to leaching either during that same irrigation event or by subsequent events. This is why knowledge of the crop root zone is important for optimum fertilizer management. It is very important to monitor the application of water and to realize that fertilizer application is linked to water application (Locascio et al. 1989).

When injecting fertilizer in noncontinuous (bulk) fashion, such as once per day or once per week, it is important to keep in mind a few pointers about the operational sequences for the injection events. The drip irrigation system should always be brought up to operating pressure prior to injecting any fertilizer or

chemical. After the system has been fully pressurized, the fertilizer can be injected. When injection is complete, the drip irrigation system should be operated for a period of time to ensure that all nutrients are out of the tubes and into the soil. This period might be the next irrigation cycle of the day if that water will not contain fertilizer.

With these operational constraints in mind, it becomes very important to design the drip irrigation system so that fertilizer injection can be achieved in a reasonable amount of time without the risk of overwatering the crop to get the fertilizer applied. Injection pumps, pipe sizes, and injection rates must be properly sized to be able to apply the nutrients in the desired amount of time and allow the system to be flushed without applying excess water during the injection and subsequent cycles.

Completely soluble fertilizers should be used through the irrigation system. Best results have been achieved in the Northeast by using a 1-1-1 ($N-P_2O_5-K_2O$) ratio soluble fertilizer. If needed, low rates of soluble essential micronutrients may also be delivered through the drip irrigation system. Including boron with the soluble $N-P_2O_5-K_2O$ fertilizer through the drip irrigation system on sandy loam or lighter-textured soils that test low to low-medium in boron has produced good results.

Some growers apply 25–40% of the season's N needs and all of the needed P and K preplant, and then the remaining N through the drip irrigation system periodically during the growing season. Research in the Northeast has shown that drip fertilizing (fertigation) with N only produces inferior results compared to applying a complete fertilizer ($N-P_2O_5-K_2O$) through the drip irrigation, particularly when the macro (major) plant nutrients are applied in a 1-1-1 ratio.

Some growers prefer to fertigate with low rates of fertilizer on a frequent or continuous basis throughout the growing season. This method is probably advantageous in very coarse, low-cation-exchange-capacity (CEC) soils that have little ability to retain the applied essential plant nutrients. In the Northeast, where soils have fair to good CEC, it is recommended that heavier rates of fertigated fertilizer be applied several times throughout the growing season, depending on the crop being grown.

Other fertilizer application methods include injecting the nutrients during the latter part of each of the irrigation cycles, keeping in mind that enough time must be left after the fertilizer injection to flush the system. An alternate method, where several irrigation cycles are used daily, is to inject fertilizer during one of the irrigation cycles. In this case, it is important to ensure that nutrients applied in one cycle are not leached by successive water applications.

The duration of nutrient injections should be long enough to allow uniform application of nutrients. For example, it is not acceptable to inject nutrients so rapidly that a large amount of nutrients is injected into the system under a short (few-minute) period. It would be more appropriate to inject nutrients over a 15- or 20-minute period followed by a 15- or 20-minute flushing period. Research on sandy soils in Florida shows that 45 minutes (for a young tomato crop) up to 1.5 hours (for a mature crop) is sufficient to apply the amount of water required by the crop during any one irrigation cycle (Smajstrla 1985b, Clark et al. 1990a). Irrigation cycles longer than 1.5 hours on a mature crop run the risk of leaching nutrients and moving water below the root zone. It should be apparent from the above discussions that water application and fertilizer application are inextricably linked.

Nutrient Injection Scheduling

Crop Growth Curve

Injecting fertilizer into a drip irrigation system offers the benefit of applying nutrients to a crop at times when they are most likely to be absorbed by the plant. The most efficient technique for scheduling nutrient applications is to follow the crop nutrient demand during the season. Generally, this means beginning early in the crop cycle with small amounts of nutrients and then increasing the rate of application of the nutrients as the crop growth rate increases and the demand increases. Once the crop has reached maturity (for example, tomatoes at first harvest), nutrient applications can level off and may even be slightly decreased toward the end of the crop. This leveling off and reduction of nutrients coincides with slowing crop growth and translocation of absorbed nutrients from the vegetative part of the plant into the fruits. Plant growth follows what is called a sigmoid curve—dry matter accumulation begins slowly, proceeds at a relatively slow rate for two to three weeks following plant emergence, and then becomes rapid for a period before crop growth begins to level off.

Therefore, an important aim for scheduling nutrients is to supply them according to the growth rate of the plant. This means that growers should understand the growth rate of the particular crop they are growing for the particular season (fall, spring, or winter). It is important, however, to schedule the injections so that they will be in the soil at the time the projected growth rate changes will be occurring. Research shows that there are probably very few adjustments that need to be made during the growth cycle for vegetables. Growers can begin the season with small amounts of nutrients and maintain the same injection rate for several weeks. When the change is made to a higher rate of injection, the higher rate can be maintained again for several weeks. For most vegetables, there will probably be at most four or five changes in the rate of injection of nutrients during the crop's cycle. For some of the fast-growing and short-season crops such as summer squash, there may be only three or four changes in the injection rate during the season.

Accounting for Preplant Nitrogen and Potassium

When N and K are applied as preplant fertilizer at the rate of approximately 20–40% of the total N and K crop nutrient needs, then the N and K injections can be delayed. This delay may be up to about two weeks after transplanting depending on the crop. When N and K are added to the soil before planting by banding near the transplant or seed, then this amount of N and K will suffice for early seedling development. If no fertilizer is placed in the bed, then nutrient injections will need to begin immediately after transplanting the crop or at seedling emergence.

Florida Schedules: An Example

As an example, the schedules for injecting N and K for vegetables in Florida appear in table 4-1 (page 42). These schedules are based on research and commercial grower experience. For some crop groups, such as the melons, extrapolations of nutrient programs for one crop to another are possible. The schedules in table 4-1 assume that the soil will be supplying none of the K crop nutrient requirement. It is important to keep in mind that the actual K amount used in a grower situation will depend on the soil test index for K. It is likely that, in many situations, the actual K amount that the grower needs to apply is less than those amounts specified in table 4-1.

TABLE 4-1

Injection schedules for mulched vegetables in Florida

CROP	METHOD OF ESTABLISHMENT[1]	TYPICAL BED SPACING (feet)	TOTAL NUTRITION [2] (pounds/acre)		CROP DEVELOPMENT [3]		INJECTION RATE [4] (pounds/acre/day)
			N	K_2O	STAGE	WEEKS	N and K_2O
Muskmelon	Transplant	5	150	150	1	2	1.0
					2	3	2.0
					3	3	2.5
					4	2	1.0
					5	2	1.0
Cucumber	Seed	5	150	150	1	1	1.0
					2	2	2.0
					3	6	2.5
					4	1	2.0
Eggplant	Transplant	6	160	150	1	2	1.0
					2	2	1.5
					3	6	2.5
Pepper	Transplant	6	175	175	1	2	1.0
					2	2	1.5
					3	7	2.5
					4	1	1.5
					5	1	1.0
Tomato	Transplant	6	175	225	1	2	1.0
					2	2	1.5
					3	7	2.5
					4	1	1.5
					5	1	1.0
Watermelon	Seed	8	150	150	1	2	1.0
					2	2	1.5
					3	4	2.5
					4	3	1.5
					5	2	1.0

SOURCE: Hochmuth et al. 1989, Hochmuth 1990a, Hochmuth 1990b, Hochmuth 1990c, Kidder et al. 1989

[1] Establishment method (seed or transplant) might affect the schedule. Transplanting shortens the growth cycle and the injection schedule by one to two weeks compared to seeding.
[2] Includes any starter fertilizer.
[3] Crop development stage and length of that stage in weeks starting from planting date.
[4] Where 20% of N and K_2O have been applied as starter, the first one or two weeks' injections can be omitted. For extended-season crops, N maintenance applications can proceed at 1.0–1.5 pounds/acre/day. Tissue testing should be used to fine tune amounts.

Rates of soluble fertilizers applied through the drip irrigation system are determined on a 3-foot soil surface area under the plastic mulch, even though the crops are grown on 5-foot rows (Garrison et al. 1999). For vine crops such as muskmelons and watermelons, the drip fertilization applications are determined on a 3-foot-wide mulched surface area on a 6-foot row.

A fertilized-mulched acre is an acre (43,560 square feet) of fertilized, mulched soil. A fertilized-mulched acre is the surface area of soil covered by the mulch.

For example, when 4-foot-wide plastic is laid on 5-foot row centers with 6 inches of each edge buried, 2 feet of the 5-foot row is uncovered and 3 feet is covered with mulch. This means that $3/5$ or 60% of the field is mulched and fertilized with the drip irrigation system. All recommendations for fertilization through drip are based on a fertilized-mulched acre.

The complete drip fertilization recommendation for bell peppers is described in this section as an example, with calculations shown in the box below.

CALCULATING FERTILIZER FOR DRIP IRRIGATION UNDER MULCH

1. First, determine the number of fertilized-mulched acres in the field using the following formula:

$$\frac{\text{Width of soil surface covered by mulch (feet)}}{\text{Row center width (feet)}} \quad \text{x field acres} \quad = \text{Fertilized-mulched acres}$$

$$\text{Example:} \quad \frac{3 \text{ feet}}{5 \text{ feet}} \quad \text{x 10 field acres} \quad = 6 \text{ fertilized-mulched acres}$$

To calculate the linear feet of mulched row:

43,560 square feet/field acre ÷ 5-foot row width = 8,712 linear feet/field acre

8,712 linear feet/field acre x 10 field acres = 87,120 linear feet

2. Second, calculate the fertilizer requirements for a fertilized-mulched acre.

a. Example for a soluble dry fertilizer to be dissolved and distributed through the drip system:

If 10 pounds of nitrogen (N), 10 pounds of phosphate (P_2O_5), and 10 pounds of potash (K_2O) per fertilized-mulched acre per application are recommended, select a dry, completely soluble fertilizer with a 1-1-1 ratio, such as 20-20-20. To determine the amount of 20-20-20 needed per fertilized-mulched acre, multiply the percentage of N, P_2O_5, or K_2O contained in the fertilizer by the quantity (pounds of fertilizer).

$$20\% \text{ N in fertilizer} \quad \text{x} \quad \frac{100\text{-pound bag}}{\text{of fertilizer}} \quad = \quad \frac{20 \text{ pounds of N in a 100-pound}}{\text{bag of 20-20-20}}$$

10 pounds N per fertilized-mulched acre are recommended, therefore,
50 pounds of 20-20-20 are needed per application.

b. Example for a liquid fertilizer distributed through the drip system:

Assume the same 10 pounds N-P_2O_5-K_2O are needed and a 10-10-10 liquid fertilizer is used. If a gallon of this fertilizer weighs 10 pounds, then 10 gallons of 10-10-10 liquid fertilizer per fertilized-mulched acre per application is required, as shown by the following calculations:

(continued on the next page)

1 gallon (10 pounds) of 10-10-10 contains: 10 pounds x 0.10 (10% N) = 1 pound N in each gallon

$$\frac{10 \text{ pounds N per fertilized-mulched acre needed}}{1 \text{ pound N in 1 gallon of 10-10-10}} = 10 \text{ gallons of 10-10-10 needed per fertilized-mulched acre}$$

3. An optional method for calculating fertilizer rates through drip under mulch is show below:

When mulched beds are on 5-foot centers with 3 feet of the soil surface covered by mulch, the pounds of nutrients or fertilizer per mulched acre can be converted to pounds per linear foot of mulched row. A mulched acre on 5-foot centers has 8,712 linear feet of mulched row. (See example #1 above for the calculation.)

Example: If 10 pounds of N, P_2O_5, and K_2O are to be applied (equal to 50 pounds of 20-20-20 per fertilized-mulched acre, as shown in example #2a above), then apply 50 pounds 20-20-20 per 8,712 linear feet, or 5.7 pounds of 20-20-20 per 1,000 linear feet of mulched row.

Before mulching, adjust soil pH to around 6.5 and then apply enough farm-grade fertilizer to supply 50 pounds per acre of N, P_2O_5, and K_2O and thoroughly incorporate into the soil. If soil tests show medium or lower levels of soil K, apply a fertilizer with a ratio of 1-1-2 or 1-1-3, carrying 50 pounds of N per acre. After mulching and installing the drip irrigation system, apply completely soluble fertilizers to supply 30 pounds of N, P_2O_5, and K_2O per fertilized-mulched acre, or 2.1 pounds of N, P_2O_5, and K_2O per 1,000 linear feet of mulched row per application. On soils testing low to low–medium in boron, also include 0.25 pound of actual boron per fertilized-mulched acre in each soluble fertilizer application.

The first soluble fertilizer application should be applied through the drip irrigation system within one week after field-transplanting peppers. The same rate of soluble fertilizer should be applied about every three weeks during the growing season for a total of six applications through the drip irrigation system. Alternatively, the fertilizer may be delivered in 12 equally timed applications throughout the growing season, provided the soluble nutrients are applied at half the above suggested rates per application so that the total seasonal rates of N, P_2O_5, and K_2O (and boron) are the same.

Note: The rates of soluble fertilizers recommended above were developed on sandy loam soils with a cation exchange capacity (CEC) of 3–5 (milliequivalents per 100 grams of oven-dry soil). If your soil has a lower CEC, it may be beneficial to increase the total seasonal soluble fertilizer nutrient rates by at least one-third. On very coarse, very low-CEC soils, it may be profitable to increase the total seasonal soluble fertilizer nutrient rates by two-thirds over the amounts recommended above. On heavier-textured soils with a CEC above 8, it may be profitable to decrease the total seasonal soluble fertilizer nutrients by one-half to three-quarters. On heavy-textured soils with a high CEC, the total seasonal plant nutrient requirement can be applied preplant (according to a soil test) before applying the plastic mulch and installing the drip irrigation system; subsequently, apply only water through the irrigation system as needed throughout the growing season.

Water Management in Relation to Fertilizer Injection

Water management and fertilizer management are linked. Changes in one of the programs will affect the efficiency of the other program. As mentioned earlier, amounts of water to be applied need to be carefully gauged with the fertilizer injection so that excess water is not applied that would result in leaching of fertilizer nutrients. Leaching potential is high for the mobile nutrients in the soil. These nutrients include N in particular, and K to a lesser degree.

Summary

Drip irrigation is an excellent tool for increasing the efficiency of a vegetable fertilizer application program. It is a tool, but not an end, for increasing fertilizer efficiency. As a tool, it must be managed efficiently to achieve the potential benefits.

CHAPTER 5

Season-Extension Technology — Row Covers and High Tunnels

Otho S. Wells and John W. Bartok, Jr.

For centuries, a wide variety of techniques have been used to extend the growing season of horticultural crops. Glass jars, glass cloches, hotcaps, cold frames, hotbeds, and greenhouses of various types have all contributed to season extension. More recently, row covers and high tunnels have become popular with growers because of their simplicity and effectiveness in protecting crops from low temperatures in both spring and fall.

Row covers and high tunnels do not offer the precision of conventional greenhouses for environmental control, but they do sufficiently modify the environment to enhance crop growth, yield, and quality. Although they provide some frost protection, their primary function is to elevate temperatures a few degrees each day over a period of several weeks.

In addition to temperature control, there are benefits of wind and rain protection; soil warming; and, in some cases, control of insects, diseases, and predators such as varmints and birds. Overall, row covers and high tunnels should be considered protective growing systems that enhance earliness, increase yields, improve quality, and reduce the use of pesticides (in some cases).

Row covers and high tunnels have sufficient versatility to make them useful on a diversity of crops and in various cropping systems. Vegetables, small fruits, and flowers are all suited to these growing systems, but the specific crops that might be grown will to a large extent depend on marketing opportunities for individual crops by individual growers.

Row Covers

There are two types of row covers: hoop-supported and floating. Hoop-supported covers, sometimes referred to as low tunnels or mini tunnels, generally cover a single row, whereas floating covers lie directly over the crop and may cover multiple rows. There are also two basic types of row-cover materials: clear polyethylene plastic and spunbonded polyester/polypropylene, both of which are available in varying thicknesses, weights, widths, lengths, and ventilation configurations.

Hoop-Supported Covers (Low Tunnels)

These plastic covers (1.0–1.5 mils thick) are supported above the crop by wire hoops made of no. 9 or 10 wire cut to lengths of 65–72 inches (photo 5-1). A simple way to make hoops without having to bend them is to buy a coil of wire and use bolt cutters to snip the hoops at the desired length. The ends of the hoops are inserted 6–8 inches into the soil on each side of the row so that the width of the hoop at the base is 24–36 inches, and the height at the apex of the hoop is 14–

Photo 5-1. Slit plastic row covers with wire hoops and black plastic mulch on summer squash. This crop matured three weeks earlier than uncovered squash.

18 inches. The hoops are spaced about 4 feet apart in the row. There are many variations of these dimensions depending on crop size. Hoops made from a coil of wire are installed by hand. For machine-installed hoops, the wire has to be straight to feed into the machine properly. For most crops grown with hoop-supported covers, black plastic mulch is used over the soil for weed control as well as for improved crop growth.

After the hoops are set, the plastic cover is applied and secured by burying the edges with soil. A small trench on either side of the row will help with this task. The cover should be taut to prevent flapping in the wind. An alternative way of securing the cover is to insert an outer wire hoop over the inner hoop with a solid (nonperforated) plastic cover that is wedged between the two hoops. With this double-hoop technique, the edges of the plastic are not buried so that the cover can be raised and lowered for ventilation.

Another method of covering is to use plastic with slits or perforations (³⁄₈-inch holes). Generally, daytime opening is not required, although at night there is a greater heat loss through the vented covering than through solid plastic. The advantage of perforated plastic is the elimination of labor for manual ventilation. The perforations also guard against sudden spikes in temperature under conditions in which a grower is not able to manually ventilate. Daytime opening is necessary for crops such as tomatoes and pepper if the temperature under the cover is expected to exceed 90°F for several hours. Under such conditions, the easiest way to ventilate quickly is to make long slits at the top of the low tunnel or use a propane burner to make large holes along the sides. This should be done in anticipation of the high temperatures, not after the potential for damage has occurred. Cucurbits (melons, cucumbers, and squash) are more tolerant of high temperatures.

Depending on the crop and the environmental conditions, the covers are left in place for three to four weeks and then removed. For crops requiring bee pollination, the covers are removed around the appearance of the first female flowers. For wind-pollinated crops (such as tomato, pepper, and eggplant), the time of removal is somewhat temperature-dependent, since temperatures should not exceed 90°F at the late-bud to open-flower stage for more than a few hours.

Floating Row Covers

For most crops, floating covers require no support because they are lightweight (photo 5-2). They "float" or lie directly over the crop, whether the crop is direct-seeded or transplanted. Materials include perforated plastic, spunbonded polyester, and spunbonded polypropylene. They do not impede seedling emergence or subsequent growth of the crop. (For an exception, see below.) To secure the cover against wind, all the edges are buried or weighted down with sandbags, stones, or other materials.

Photo 5-2. Slit plastic with hoops (center row) and spunbonded floating covers on either side.

There are two types of floating covers: perforated polyethylene, which is about 1 mil thick, and spunbonded polyester or polypropylene, which is available in several weights (not thicknesses).

Perforated polyethylene has a uniform pattern of ³⁄₈-inch holes (74 holes per square foot) for ventilation. However, the holes allow for heat loss at night and can be an entry point for insects. Overall, many growers have found these covers to be very beneficial for growth enhancement (photo 5-3, page 48).

Spunbonded covers are composed of a thin mesh of white synthetic fibers, which entrap heat and serve as a barrier to wind, insects, and varmints (photo 5-4, page 48). Water from rain or overhead irrigation freely passes through. The weight of these covers ranges from 0.3 to about 2.0 ounces per square yard (10–68 grams per square meter). The lightest covers are used primarily for insect exclusion while the heaviest are used for frost protection. The most common weights are 0.5 to 1.25 ounces per square yard (17–42 grams per

Photo 5-3. This cauliflower was covered at seeding with a 30-foot-wide floating perforated polyethylene row cover.

Photo 5-4. Spunbonded covers are lightweight and transparent to light. They entrap heat and protect against wind, heavy rain, and insects. The crop is green beans.

only the edges are secured. These covers vary in width from 6 to 50 feet and are up to about 800 feet long. One way to evaluate labor needs is to compare the time that it takes to apply one piece of cover 50 feet wide x 200 feet long (500 perimeter feet) versus the time it takes to apply five pieces that are 10 feet wide x 200 feet long (2,100 perimeter feet). Regardless of width, the cover is secured by weighting down the edges (sides and ends) with soil, sandbags, stones, or long pins. In extremely windy areas, additional weighting in the middle of the cover is advisable (photo 5-5).

Generally, when the covers are draped (not pulled tight) over the soil, there is sufficient slack to allow for crop growth without causing deformation of the plants. For many crops, such as beets, carrots, radish, lettuce, and other salad greens, the covers may be left on until harvest. However, for longer-season crops or tall crops such as sweet corn, the covers will need to be removed after three to four weeks, or additional slack will need to be provided by burying an extra amount of row cover along one edge. Then the cover is loosened as the crop grows.

Insect control is effective with spunbonded covers when all of the edges are completely sealed. For example, maggots in radish (and in other crops in the cabbage family) are controlled when a cover is applied at seeding with a complete seal around the edges. When the adult maggot flies search out the young seed-

square meter). With covers under 0.5 ounce, there is minimal heat retention at night; over 1.25 ounce, there is a significant reduction in light transmission. The heavy covers (over 1.25 ounce) are used for nighttime frost protection only, since they do not transmit sufficient light for optimum crop growth.

Spunbonded row covers in the 0.5- to 1.25-ounce range provide 2°–4°F frost protection in the spring (figure 5-1). In the fall, there is more protection, because there is a larger reservoir of heat in the soil in the fall than in the spring. These covers perform very well in protecting late-season tomatoes and pepper from early frosts.

Floating covers require much less installation labor than hoop-supported covers. The wider and longer the covers, the less labor is required per unit area, since

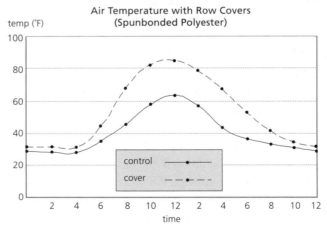

Figure 5-1. Row covers provide a few degrees of frost protection at night but give large temperature increases during the day. The data were taken during a clear day and night in Durham, New Hampshire.

Photo 5-5. This wide spunbonded floating cover was installed over sweet corn the day of planting. The edges are well-secured with soil.

lings for laying eggs, the flies will be unable to get under or through the cover. A continuous furrow of soil along the edges is probably the best sealing method.

It is feasible, however, that row covers could actually increase insect damage on some crops. The environment under the cover is pretty ideal for insects, so it is important that all transplants that are to be covered are free of insects, such as aphids and whiteflies, at transplanting. To prevent a heavy population of Colorado potato beetles under a cover, do not plant potatoes in the same place in successive years, and use a cover the second year. Overwintering adult beetles could emerge from the soil under the cover and lay an abundance of eggs, which would soon hatch into a dense population of larvae.

There are a couple of disadvantages of floating covers. One is weed pressure under the covers. Between strips of plastic mulch, or with crops such as sweet corn where plastic mulch is not used, weeds grow rapidly and competitively. When using herbicides, the highest labeled rate is generally recommended to adequately control weeds. Even though weed growth under floating covers is accelerated, mechanical or chemical weeding is easily accommodated by partial removal of the cover. By leaving only one edge secured, the cover can be pulled back and replaced as necessary. There is also some inefficiency in covering the space between rows covered with plastic mulch. But here again, the trade-off is reduced installation labor of wide covers versus narrow covers.

Row Cover Crops

Most all vegetable crops as well as strawberries, raspberries, and cut flowers have been grown with row covers. Although the primary crops for row cover use are high-value crops such as melons, tomatoes, pepper, summer squash, sweet corn, salad crops, and strawberries, many growers find row covers to be valuable for a number of crops for varying reasons—earliness, higher yields, overwintering protection, and insect and varmint control. Crop selection and cover selection are important to the economical success of the extra inputs. Crop characteristics such as temperature sensitivity, pollination methods, and growth habit all dictate the type of row cover that is best to use.

Even though most crops can be grown without damage under floating covers, tomatoes, pepper, and summer squash are exceptions. If the spunbonded material is not supported with wire hoops for these crops, flapping of the cover in the wind will damage the growing points of young plants. Also, with summer squash under windy conditions, many of the leaves might be broken by the cover. For these three crops, a series of strategically placed wire hoops will prevent crop damage (photo 5-6).

To some extent, floating row covers serve as a windbreak against the negative effects of wind. However, in areas of sustained high or gusty winds, the temperature benefits under spunbonded covers may be moderated due to excessive air movement under the cover. Especially under such conditions, supporting

Photo 5-6. Under windy conditions, wire hoops are used to support wide covers over summer squash.

hoops are recommended for air control as well as prevention of serious plant abrasion from undulating covers.

High Tunnels

High tunnels encompass a crop-growing system that fits somewhere between row covers and greenhouses. They are relatively inexpensive (about $1.30 per square foot, excluding labor), so high-tunnel crop production is possible with limited capital. This system is particularly appealing to new-entry growers who utilize retail marketing channels.

High Tunnel Systems

High tunnels are not conventional greenhouses. But like plastic-covered greenhouses, they are generally Quonset-shaped and are constructed of metal bows that are attached to metal posts that have been driven into the ground about 2 feet deep. They are covered with one layer of 6-mil greenhouse-grade polyethylene and are ventilated by manually rolling up the sides each morning and rolling them down in early evening (photos 5-7 and 5-8). There is no permanent heating system, although it is advisable to have a standby portable propane unit to protect against unexpected below-freezing temperatures. There are no electrical connections. The only external connection is a water supply for drip irrigation. The ends of the tunnels are framed in but constructed in such a way as to facilitate easy access into the tunnel with a small tractor and tiller or other equipment (photo 5-9).

Ventilation is provided by installing roll-up sides (photo 5-8). An 8- to 10-inch baseboard is attached to the metal posts flush with the soil surface so that surface water will not run into the tunnel. A hipboard is attached to the bows 36 to 42 inches above the baseboard. The plastic cover is attached at the hipboard with batten boards that are held with galvanized screws spaced 18–24 inches apart. The plastic is firmly sandwiched between the boards. Alternative attachment designs have been developed at The Pennsylvania State University. At the bottom edge of the plastic, which should initially extend about a foot beyond the baseboard, a 1-inch metal pipe is laid along the edge of the plastic exactly parallel to the tunnel. The edge of

Photo 5-7. The basic structure of a high tunnel—metal posts, metal bows, baseboard, and hipboard, laid out level and square.

Photo 5-8. A fully constructed high tunnel with roll-up sides adjusted in height to meet ventilation needs.

Photo 5-9. Large, hinged end sections allow for access into the tunnel with a small tractor and plastic-laying equipment (at The Pennsylvania State University).

the plastic is taped (every 12 to 18 inches) to the pipe with duct tape (or attached with plastic clips), and then the pipe is rolled to the edge of the tunnel alongside the baseboard. With a sliding "T" handle at one end of the pipe, the plastic may be rolled to any height up to the hipboard. The amount of the opening on each side will depend on the desired internal temperature, the ambient temperature, and current wind speed. Experience and a couple of maximum/minimum thermometers are the best tools for determining how to regulate temperature to fit the requirements of specific crops. For example, melons in a high tunnel will tolerate higher temperatures than broccoli.

For all practical purposes, high tunnels are field-situated, protected growing structures that should produce high economic returns. Therefore, they should be erected on the best soil—soil that is well-drained and that has had the proper pH and nutrient adjustments as for a field soil. The soil should be smooth, firm, and moist at planting. A line of drip irrigation is laid about 6 inches off-center for each row of crop (or between a double row), and then a one-piece sheet of 6-mil black plastic is laid over the total soil surface. (An exception to the black plastic would be made with direct-seeded crops such as lettuce, radish, or beets.) The black plastic is very beneficial for soil warming, reduction of evaporation of water from the soil, and weed control. It also provides a disease barrier between the soil and the plants. The plastic sheet should be anchored with metal pins and string, stones, or some other way to prevent the billowing of the plastic during brisk winds that enter through the transplanting holes.

Alternative methods have been developed at The Pennsylvania State University whereby mulch-covered raised beds with drip irrigation are made with a small bedder/mulcher machine pulled behind a small tractor (photo 5-10). The system is very similar to outdoor systems, but the important difference is the environmental protection afforded by the high tunnel.

After the drip lines and the plastic sheeting are in place, planting may commence. The specific planting design will depend on the crop, but using tomatoes as an example, the rows are 3.5 feet apart and plants are 18–24 inches apart in the row when the plants are supported with a basketweave (short-stake) trellis system.

Photo 5-10. Small plastic mulch/drip tape applicator machine used in a system at The Pennsylvania State University.

The spacing for other crops will be somewhat similar to general field planting; however, because of the economics of high-tunnel production, it is imperative that intensive culture be practiced. Because tunnel crops are protected from rain and heavy dews, the plants remain drier than when outdoors and will tolerate closer spacing.

High Tunnel Management

High tunnels are not automated. Consequently, for maximum efficiency, they require daily attention, especially in the morning and evening and during heavy rain or strong winds. Temperature and humidity are the two critical factors that should be controlled as much as possible. Early each morning, the sides should be rolled up to flush out the humidity and to keep temperature under control. The temperature in a closed high tunnel rises very rapidly on a clear morning! In other words, don't put off rolling up the sides. In early evening, roll down the sides to entrap as much heat as possible. Close the sides each evening until the night temperature reaches about 65°F. In northern states, this could mean that the sides will be rolled down each day well into the summer.

Ventilation is best accomplished when wind moves through the tunnel from side to side; therefore, orient the tunnel accordingly, if possible. The width of the tunnel also affects ventilation. It is hard to be specific on the maximum width, but experience shows that

Photo 5-11. On a warm and calm day, the sides of high tunnels are rolled up all the way. As the plants grow taller, cross-ventilation is reduced.

about 20 feet seems to be the maximum width that allows for good ventilation, especially as plants grow taller and block the cross-wise air flow (photo 5-11).

Benefits of Tunnels

The primary benefit of tunnels is earliness. Tomatoes in a high tunnel mature on average about one month before field tomatoes. Earliness is the combination of being able to plant in high tunnels about two weeks earlier than in the field and faster ripening (by about two weeks) inside the tunnel. Overall, the cost of a tunnel is recovered the first year when selling at retail prices. Table 5-1 shows a complete economic analysis of producing tomatoes in a 14-foot-by-96-foot high tunnel and illustrates annual net returns at varying yields and selling prices. At $2.00 per pound for a 3,000-pound harvest, the net return is $0.86 per pound.

Another large benefit of tunnels is disease control. The plastic cover provides shelter from rain, the plastic sheeting on the ground is a barrier against evaporation of soil moisture, and early morning ventilation reduces relative humidity. (In tropical countries, high tunnels are used primarily as rain shelters.) Because of low humidity, plant leaves remain dry, impeding the incidence and spread of disease. Early blight of tomatoes, a serious foliage and fruit disease on field tomatoes, is not a problem in high tunnels when the tunnels are vented daily.

Although tunnels do require more manual attention than greenhouses, the benefits of high tunnels in a diversified farm operation have proven to be a valu-

able asset in overcoming a short growing season. Both cool- and warm-season crops do well in the spring. With cool-season crops, the season may easily be extended into early winter and even throughout the winter for hardy salad crops (photo 5-12). Fall-planted strawberries in high tunnels ripen the following spring, about six weeks earlier than field-grown berries (photo 5-13).

Just about any field-grown crop can be profitably grown in high tunnels, including tomato, pepper, potato, vine crops, cabbage family crops, and salad and root crops (photo 5-14, page 54). Even early sweet corn is a potentially profitable crop. Long-vined pumpkins and winter squash might not be suitable. However, there is no reason to summarily exclude any crop with-

Photo 5-12. Hardy greens grown in a high tunnel.

Photo 5-13. Fall-planted strawberries on raised plastic-covered beds with drip irrigation. Plants are six weeks earlier than field-produced berries.

TABLE 5-1
Economic analysis of high-tunnel tomato production
(one tunnel, 14 feet by 96 feet = 1,344 square feet)

ANNUAL RETURNS AND EXPENSES	Amount or rate	Price or charge	Dollars
I. RECEIPTS	3,000 pounds	$2.00/pound	$6,000.00
II. MARKETING COSTS	$1,500.00	25% of price received	
III. PRODUCTION EXPENSES			
Variable costs			
Plants	240 plants	$0.20 each	$48.00
Stakes	128 stakes	$0.30 each	$38.40
String	2,500 feet	$17.00/tunnel	$17.00
Fertilizer and lime, preplant		$6.00/tunnel	$ 6.00
Fertilizer through drip irrigation		$22.00/tunnel	$22.00
Pest control, *Encarsia formosa*		$30.00/tunnel	$30.00
Basket replacement	5 baskets	$3.50 each	$17.50
Labor	111.5 hours	$11.00/hour	
4.0 hours for preplant preparation			$44.00
15.0 hours to plant, set stakes and stringing			$165.00
25.0 hours to prune, control pests, and ventilate			$275.00
17.5 hours to irrigate and fertigate			$192.50
40.0 hours to harvest (four times)			$440.00
10.0 hours for annual maintenance and cleanup			$110.00
Miscellaneous variable costs (rototiller and injector)		$15.00/tunnel	$15.00
Operating interest	$240.00	10% interest	$24.00
TOTAL variable production expenses			$1,444.40

ANNUAL RETURNS AND EXPENSES	Amount or rate	Price or charge	Dollars
Fixed costs			
Annual depreciation (zero salvage value)			
Structure	$1,860.00 investment	10 years	$186.00
Plastic	$259.00 investment	3 years	$86.33
Annual interest charge on investment			
Structure	$930.00 average investment	10% interest	$93.00
Plastic	$130.00 average investment	10% interest	$12.95
Land costs			
Interest	$420.00 investment	6% interest	$25.20
Real estate tax (share)		$15.00/tunnel	$15.00
Other fixed costs (equipment- and machine-related)		$60.00/tunnel	$60.00
TOTAL fixed production expenses			$478.49
IV. ANNUAL NET RETURNS (Receipts less marketing costs less production expenses)			$2,577.11

V. ANNUAL NET RETURNS FOR DIFFERENT PRICES AND PRODUCTION
(Marketing cost kept at $0.50/pound; net returns adjusted by $0.15/pound harvest cost)

		PRICE RECEIVED PER POUND				
		$1.50	$1.75	$2.00	$2.25	$2.50
Pounds produced	2,500	$652	$1,277	$1,902	$2,527	$3,152
	2,750	$865	$1,552	$2,240	$2,927	$3,615
	3,000	$1,077	$1,827	$2,577	$3,327	$4,077
	3,250	$1,290	$2,102	$2,915	$3,727	$4,540
	3,500	$1,502	$2,377	$3,252	$4,127	$5,002

SOURCE: Michael R. Sciabarrasi and Otho S. Wells, Extension Specialists, University of New Hampshire Cooperative Extension, September 1999.

Photo 5-14. Excellent yield and quality of green bell peppers grown in a high tunnel.

out first considering all of the ramifications of unique or niche marketing opportunities. Cut flowers, both spring-planted annuals and fall-planted bulbs, grow very nicely in high tunnels. Other possibilities include container-grown crops such as dwarf fruit trees and blueberries, raspberries, perennial flowers, and herbs.

Heating and Ventilation Alternatives

Supplemental heating is not very common with high tunnels. The basic concept of the tunnel is to extend the season without much added expense. When heating systems and mechanical ventilation are added, the cost jumps significantly and may be difficult to justify for short growing seasons. However, a low-cost root-zone heating system may have a short payback period, especially for a high-value crop such as spring tomatoes.

Heating Systems

Calculating Heater Size. If supplemental heating is desired, there are several systems that will provide heat for cool nights or short periods of time. Before choosing a heating system for a tunnel, first calculate how large a heater is required.

Heat loss can be calculated by multiplying the glazed area (in square feet) of the high tunnel by a insulation factor (1.25 for single glazing and 0.8 for double glazing) and by the temperature difference between the desired inside night temperature and the lowest outside temperature during the period of use. In the above formula, the glazed area is the total surface area covered with plastic. It includes the roof and endwalls.

Example: What size heater is needed to heat a single-glazed 14-foot-by-96-foot high tunnel to 50°F on a night when the temperature will fall to 30°F? The surface area including the top and endwalls is 2,300 square feet. The heater output, not input, can be calculated as follows:

$$\text{Heat loss} = 2300 \text{ square feet} \times 1.25 \times (50 - 30)$$
$$= 57{,}500 \text{ Btu/hour}$$

Because most heaters have about 80% efficiency, a heater with about 70,000 Btu-per-hour output is required.

A rule of thumb for calculating heat loss is to multiply the floor area of the high tunnel by $1\frac{1}{2}$, then multiply this by the degrees of protection desired. This will be the approximate heater input needed.

For highest efficiency, the high tunnel plastic covering should be tight to eliminate infiltration. Cracks around roll-up sides and door openings should be sealed.

Types of Systems. Nonvented heaters should be used only for emergency or short-term situations. Long-term use is likely to result in sulfur dioxide or ethylene gas injury to sensitive plants. Salamanders and fan-forced or convection propane heaters are available with outputs up to 400,000 Btu per hour. See appendix A, page 123, for a manufacturer of a gas unit that can heat smaller high tunnels. It has a mechanical thermostat that doesn't require electricity.

Gas or oil-fired hot-air heaters are easy to install and provide air circulation. They are generally supported on a pipe frame off the ground and directed to blow the heated air down an aisle or above the crop to avoid drying the plants.

Some growers have used a hot-air furnace connected to poly ducts that are run between the rows. Holes in the duct should be located to direct the heat to the base of the plants and not onto the foliage.

Research by Dr. Craig Storlie at Rutgers University showed that a few degrees of temperature modification can be achieved with thermal tubes filled with water placed next to the plants. The water captures heat during the day and gives it back to the air at night.

Horizontal Air Flow (HAF). To eliminate cold spots and large differences in temperature, air circulation may be desirable. The horizontal air flow (HAF) system uses small one-fifteenth-horsepower circulating fans. Fans are placed to circulate air down one side of the tunnel and back the other side. In a 14-foot-by-96-foot tunnel, locating two fans above the crop on the center frame, one pointed in one direction and the other pointed in the opposite direction, will give good results. In a 14-foot-by-48-foot tunnel, the fans should be located in opposite corners of the tunnel about 8 feet from the endwall. The fans should operate continuously, except when the sides are rolled up. Air circulation will also help reduce moisture-related disease problems.

Root-Zone Heating. Because root temperature is more critical than air temperature for most plants, root-zone heating may be the best choice.

A simple system using polyethylene pipes and a domestic hot water heater works well (figure 5-2). Water at a temperature of about 100°F is circulated through the pipes.

For soil crops, the pipes are placed 8–12 inches deep to allow rotary tilling above. Generally, one pipe is located under each row, although more runs can be installed to provide more heat. The piping is installed as loops fed by a supply header with the other end connected to a return header. Using a reverse-return system, the flow through each loop travels the same distance, providing uniform heating.

Heat loss from plastic is relatively slow, so lengths of 200 feet for 1/2-inch pipe and 400 feet for 3/4-inch pipe will give good results with minimum friction loss. Heat output is about 10 Btu per hour per linear foot of pipe.

A tank-type domestic hot water heater (30,000–40,000 Btu per hour) fired by natural gas or propane will provide the root-zone heat for a tomato crop growing area up to 6,000 square feet. Water is moved through the system with circulating pumps. A combination of root-zone and air heating will usually be needed on cold

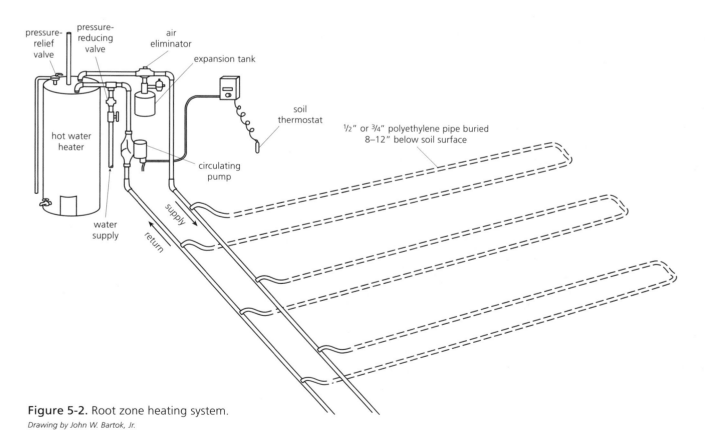

Figure 5-2. Root zone heating system.
Drawing by John W. Bartok, Jr.

nights. The system should be drained during the winter if not in use to avoid freeze damage.

Cooling Systems

Natural Ventilation. Roll-up sides are normally built into high tunnels. This is a natural ventilation system that operates on the principle that heat is removed by a pressure difference created by wind and temperature gradients. Wind plays the major role. In most cases, a wind speed of 1 mile per hour is adequate to keep the inside temperature within two degrees of ambient. There are very few days when the wind is less than 1 mile per hour, especially if the outdoor temperature is above 80°F.

Future improvements in tunnel design may include ridge vents. These vents will improve natural ventilation if they are orientated with the opening away from the prevailing wind direction so that heat is drawn out of the tunnel. Mechanically opened roof sections that allow the crop to experience outdoor conditions are also possible.

Fan Ventilation. A small fan system could be installed in one endwall to provide the initial automatic stage of cooling before the roll-up sides are opened. A motorized shutter should be located on the opposite endwall. A ¼-horsepower, 24-inch fan is adequate for a 14-foot-by-48-foot tunnel, and a ⅓-horsepower, 30-inch fan is suitable for a 14-foot-by-96-foot tunnel. Fans should be controlled by a thermostat located at plant height in the middle of the tunnel. The thermostat should be shaded from direct sunlight.

Mobile Greenhouses

A mobile greenhouse that can be moved from one site to another has several advantages over high tunnels.

Early, cool spring crops such as lettuce and cabbage can be started in the ground in the greenhouse. When the weather warms up, the greenhouse can be moved to an adjacent plot where warm-season crops such as tomatoes and melons can be started. The reverse procedure can be used in the fall.

A mobile greenhouse does not have the pest and disease buildup problems often found in permanent greenhouses. The soil can remain fallow for a season or for a year. Soil solarization can also be achieved.

Wood-frame and pipe-frame greenhouses can be made mobile. The hoops on a pipe-frame structure can be moved from one foundation or set of ground posts to another. Eliot Coleman in Harborside, Maine, has a hoophouse mounted on a track system that he pulls with a small tractor. He also has several greenhouses supported on pipe skids, bolted to the hoops. These provide support and reduce friction with the ground. This style of frame could also be moved with two winches.

Dave Chapman of East Thetford, Vermont, built a 25-foot-by-96-foot wood-frame greenhouse that moves on V-grooved wheels on angle-iron tracks. The heating system is permanently installed between two sites so that it serves the greenhouse in both locations.

Mobile greenhouses have to be adequately braced to take the stress of moving. They also have to be secured to deadmen or anchors so that they can take high winds without moving. Provisions for utility hookups at each site should be made.

Summary

Row covers and high tunnels play a distinct role in the intensive production of several horticultural crops. In general, high tunnels provide a more optimal growing environment than row covers, yet each system has its place in a diversified farming operation. The success of either system depends on how a grower integrates it with other production methods and marketing schemes. An outstanding benefit of both row covers and high tunnels is their flexibility of design and size that will easily accommodate the needs of individual farm operations.

CHAPTER 6

Windbreaks

Robert Rouse and Laurie Hodges

Windbreaks are an important and often over-looked component of a plasticulture system. They provide benefits regardless of where you farm or what crops you are raising. When wind protection is included in a plasticulture production system, crops benefit from less wind stress and an improved micro-climate for growth and development. There is less crop injury due to soil abrasion or wind-whipping of plants, less extreme soil temperature fluctuations, and im-proved soil warming. Wind protection often results in earlier yields of higher-quality crops.

The Problem

Vegetables in general have a very low tolerance to wind stress (table 6-1). Wind is not only a concern in horti-cultural production along the coasts; it is a problem wherever crops are grown—in mountainous areas, along river valleys, and in the middle west and central plains. The preferred soils for horticultural crop pro-duction are light, sandy, well-drained soils. Crops on these soils are very likely to respond positively to in-tensive plasticulture production systems. However, these soils are also most subject to soil erosion by wind. Consequently, crops grown on these sites will be sub-ject to the adverse effects of wind for at least part of the growing season.

There are two factors to consider regarding wind stress. One is direct physical injury or abrasion caused by windblown soil or abrasion from leaves or other plant parts rubbing against each other. Fine soil par-ticles, both organic and mineral, are easily moved by wind. Often these particles contain 10 to 20 times as much humus and phosphate as the heavier particles that stay on the field. Many growers have seen sandy soils blowing across rows covered with plastic mulch.

TABLE 6-1		
Threshold wind velocity for selected crops		
THRESHOLD WIND VELOCITY (miles per hour)		
Crop	Physiological injury	Mechanical injury
Cotton	≥13	≥13.4
Corn	9–13	13.4
Milo	≥9	≥13.4
Cucumber	≥9	>11.0
Pepper	≥9	>11.0
Cabbage	≥9	>11.0
Wheat	≥7	≥13.4

SOURCE: Wei Lin and Jiang Ailiang, 1987. Kexue Tongbao 32:605–609.

When young, tender plants are either transplanted or direct-seeded and emerge early in the season on plas-tic mulched beds, and there is potential for problems if winds are not controlled. When plants are more mature, winds may cause them to lodge, break, or lose fruit. Plants can be uprooted from the planting hole by a combination of wind and soil erosion in a plasti-culture system. Wind-stressed fields may experience more disease.

The second factor is that of the indirect effects of wind on plant physiology and on the environment immediately around the plant (the microclimate). Reports indicate that the potential for reduced yields of vegetable crops occurs when wind velocity exceeds approximately 9 miles per hour. You may not notice differences in pollination or fertilization, the rate of growth, or crop quality unless you have a comparable field or growing area that is protected from the wind. Also, the effect of wind stress on young plants may become evident only after several weeks of exposure.

For example, young tomato transplants had significantly more catfacing when they were exposed to as little as 7.5 minutes of 30-mile-per-hour wind (Greig et al. 1974). At the physiological level, you may not notice any crop injury. However, wind increases transpiration and changes plant water status. Typically, plants exposed to winds are shorter and have thicker leaves than those protected from wind stresses. Leafy greens raised with wind protection may be of higher quality—sweeter and more tender—than those with full exposure to winds.

Younger plants are more susceptible to wind injury than older, more established plants. Unfortunately, the seasons with the highest and most frequent winds often coincide with the use of young transplants in plasticulture systems. One secret for successful production of high yields of high-quality marketable fruit is to reduce wind stress through the use of natural or artificial windbreaks or shelterbelts.

Some of the problems associated with wind are obvious, some are not so obvious. Several are discussed below.

Abrasion Injury

When mechanical wind injury is considered, growers are usually concerned about soil erosion and plant abrasion by the soil particles. The "sandblasting" of newly transplanted vegetable crops can lead to injury, disease, or death, depending on the severity and duration of the damage.

As mentioned earlier, sandy soils are prime candidates for plasticulture production systems. They also have a more limited water-holding capacity and will dry out quickly. Dry, sandy soils are very subject to wind erosion. Smaller particles such as silts and clays can be blown at lower wind speeds. Muck soils, which are high in organic matter, can also have severe wind erosion problems as they dry. Soil erosion is more likely in large open fields than small protected ones. Soil does not ordinarily blow until wind velocity approaches 12–13 miles per hour 1 foot above the soil surface. This is known as the threshold erosion velocity, and the ability for the wind to carry soil is proportional to the cube of the wind's velocity. Therefore, if there is a small reduction in the wind speed, there is a greater proportionate reduction in the rate of soil loss.

Sand abrasion injury can cause total death of the plant if the injury is severe enough. Growth may be slowed or altered if meristem tissue is injured, resulting in more branching and delayed maturity. Wounds on leaf surfaces caused by windblown soil or leaf-to-leaf abrasion can provide entry points for plant pathogens, especially bacterial pathogens carried on windblown rain, irrigation water, or soil.

Windblown soil not only damages crops and reduces soil fertility but also fills up ditches, both drainage and irrigation. It can also pile up along fences or rows and on roadways. Blowing soil can and does limit visibility and leads to hazardous highway driving conditions.

Remember, as wind speeds increase, direct damage by wind becomes more of a problem. In the United States, wind speeds of 20–45 miles per hour, with higher-velocity gusts of wind, can occur during the growing season due to passing storms or weather fronts.

Wind-Whipping

Wind-whipping can be a severe problem in vine crops, sometimes leading to plant death. It can be more of a problem for vine crops grown on raised plastic-mulched beds. The situation becomes more acute as young plants start to vine or run. Wind blowing in one direction will blow and twist the vines. Many times, the wind direction changes abruptly, turning and twisting the vines. This can place extreme pressure on the stem near the soil line. The stem may crack and break. Entire plants have been twisted or broken off at the soil line by wind action. In other cases, young melon plants have been pulled from the soil by the force of the wind.

Lodging

Lodging is the flattening of a crop by strong winds. This phenomenon often occurs when winds accompany or follow a heavy rain. It is a problem in corn or heavily fruited crops. Strong winds can cause an entire length of staked tomato plants loaded with fruit to fall like dominos.

When crops are trellised or staked, damage from moderate winds can be overcome with adequate end bracing and breaks in the staked system. Using larger-diameter stakes at the end rows provides greater stability to the staked system. Some growers use reinforcement bars (rebar) to increase stability of trellising systems. Breaking up the rows with picker crossovers every 100 feet will help.

Lodged plants are harder to harvest, may fall over the raised beds into the alleys, and may produce more cull fruit. Including windbreaks at regular intervals perpendicular to the prevailing winds across a field can reduce lodging and increase harvest labor efficiency and marketable yields.

Plant Damage and Disease Potential

Plants damaged or wounded by the mechanical effects of wind have more entry points for pathogens, especially bacteria. Shelter from wind, windblown rain, and windblown soil particles can reduce the incidence of disease.

One example of this involves strawberries. Strong spring winds can have a desiccating effect on uncovered strawberry plasticulture plants. The leaves can be scorched brown, causing them to die. The dead leaves, if not removed, can be a haven for gray mold *Botrytis cinerea,* which, if conditions are right, can devastate a strawberry crop. In a research trial at the University of Nebraska, bell peppers in wind-exposed plots had ten times more bacterial leaf spot than peppers planted with wind protection.

In cropping systems, some air movement is desirable to dry plant foliage quickly after rain, dew, or irrigation to minimize disease potential. But too much air movement can injure plants or their fruit.

Wind Stress

Although reducing wind erosion and associated plant abrasion is often the primary reason for using windbreaks, simple wind stress cannot be ignored. In general, the threshold wind speed resulting in decreased vegetable yields is about 9 miles per hour. Many studies have shown growth effects at wind velocities less than this. Table 6-2 shows the effect that different wind speeds can have on plants.

Grains and grasses are more tolerant to wind stress and abrasion than vegetables—thus their suitability for use in annual windbreak systems. Some field reports indicate that solanaceous crops such as peppers, tomatoes, and eggplants are more sensitive to wind stress than other vegetables, with reported thresholds for yield reduction at wind velocities as low as 4.5 miles per hour. Other reports indicate that crops grown for vegetative parts, such as leafy greens or asparagus, may be more sensitive than those grown for reproductive

TABLE 6-2
Wind speed and the effect upon plants

| | WIND SPEED | | | |
	kilometers/hour	meters/second	miles/hour	EFFECT
Calm	0–2	0.56	1.26	Smoke rises vertically.
Light air	2–6	1.68	3.78	Smoke drifts.
Light breeze	7–12	3.36	7.56	Leaf movement.
Gentle breeze	13–19	5.32	11.97	Small twigs in motion.
Moderate breeze	20–29	8.12	18.27	Small branches move.
Fresh breeze	30–39	10.92	24.57	Small trees with leaves begin to sway.
Strong breeze	40–50	14.0	31.5	Large branches move.
Gales	51–100	28	63	At lower speeds, leaves are blown off; whole trees in motion. At moderate speeds, twigs and branches break. At high speeds, trees can be uprooted.
Storm	101–120	33.6	75.6	Severe damage; trees can be uprooted.
Hurricane, typhoon	> 120	>33.6	>75.6	Extensive damage/ trees can be uprooted.

structures, such as tomatoes, peppers, and beans. Still other reports indicate that cucumbers and squashes may tolerate more wind damage than muskmelons and watermelons.

To date, these observations have not been substantiated by research. But considering the low wind velocities that result in significant yield reduction or crop injury, growers should include wind protection regardless of the crop being grown.

Increased Transpiration and Evaporation

Wind can increase transpiration, or plant moisture loss that occurs through the leaves and other plant parts. Abrasion or wounding of the plant stem and leaf cuticle increases water loss from the plant. This additional moisture loss can have a very negative impact, especially on a new vegetable transplant or seedling that has a reduced root area and limited ability to take up soil moisture. More mature plants will need more irrigation to compensate for the loss.

Excess water loss through the plant leaves can lead to desiccation and leaf scorch or dieback, nature's way of equalizing water uptake with water loss. With plug transplants, it is critical to have good soil coverage over the plug root ball. Exposed peat pots or plug plant mix can act like a wick, drying the root ball and causing plant desiccation and death. The reduced root area and uptake function of new transplants coupled with cool or cold, wet soils can result in very little new root growth and development. Microclimate modification is critical to overcome these negatives, and wind protection and windbreaks can help greatly in this regard.

Microclimate Alteration

Whatever heat may be retained by soil, soil moisture, and plants on a sunny day can be removed rapidly by wind. One reason growers use plastic mulch is that it absorbs heat during the day and retains much of that heat in the soil during the night. The effect of warming the soil promotes plant growth and earlier crop maturity. By reducing air movement and heat transfer from the soil to the air at night, windbreaks also promote earlier crop maturity. Typically, air above a sheltered crop is 2°–3°F warmer than above a comparable, unsheltered area. The reduction of wind velocity by wind barriers has many ramifications on the microclimate of the protected zone, especially air temperature, soil temperature, and relative humidity in the crop canopy.

Dry air can reduce the effectiveness of pollination and result in lower yields of marketable fruit. Reducing wind and air movement within the crop canopy leads to higher relative humidity surrounding the floral parts than for wind-exposed plants, resulting in better fertilization and improvements in marketable yields. With a plasticulture system in place, crop transpiration will contribute to the relative humidity in the crop canopy, but less water will be lost by evaporation directly from the soil. The benefits of wind protection on crops grown under arid and semi-arid conditions can be significant.

Lost Income

Summing up all the effects of wind stress and abrasion, it comes back to a matter of dollars lost. Wind stress slows crop development and time to market and increases water use. Under windy conditions, fruit size, color, and flavor may be adversely affected. Delayed time to market usually has an adverse effect on profit. Abrasion or scarring on the saleable part of any commodity will result in lower grades and more culls. To achieve the maximum potential from crops grown in a plasticulture system, it is imperative to include windbreaks to minimize these deleterious effects of wind stress and wind erosion. The rest of this chapter is devoted to solutions to the problems associated with wind in plasticulture production systems.

The Solution: Windbreaks

Windbreaks, either temporary or permanent, are needed to limit the impact of wind on a crop. Specific guidelines exist for each type of windbreak regarding its appropriateness for different situations. For further assistance, contact your local soil conservation program or Cooperative Extension office. Some general principles are discussed in the following sections.

A windbreak is an obstruction that is placed in the path of a wind flow and causes an alteration in the wind velocity. Windbreaks are most effective when they are perpendicular to the wind flow. As wind strikes a windbreak, it must move over, through, or around the obstruction. This alternation in wind direction creates a small area on the windward side of the windbreak and a larger area on its leeward side that is protected from the full force of the wind. The extent of the leeward protection is related to the height of the windbreak.

As wind passes over a windbreak, turbulent currents that are of a lower velocity than the main wind stream are created when the air that is forced over the windbreak descends to meet the air that was forced through the windbreak. At the ends of the windbreak, eddy currents form as air moves through the openings between rows or windbreak systems. The wind velocity in these eddy zones may be higher than the unobstructed wind.

Windbreaks that are impenetrable to air also create a strong vacuum on their protected leeward side that tends to pull or suck the obstructed wind stream into the protected zone. This reduces the level of leeward protection afforded by the windbreak. Windbreaks that allow some wind penetration reduce the vacuum and consequently improve the windbreak's effectiveness.

The objectives in designing a windbreak for crop protection are: (1) to achieve enough height to create protection for the desired distance on the leeward side of the windbreak; and (2) to achieve enough penetrability to reduce the effects of eddy currents and the leeward vacuum, yet still afford the desired amount of wind protection and wind speed reduction.

Wind erosion is a function of the length of the unobstructed area along the direction of the prevailing wind (that is, parallel to the wind). Sometimes this is assumed to be the "width" of the field. As this distance increases, the amount of wind erosion increases. Windbreaks break up the field into smaller fields (or wind runs) and thereby reduce the length factor in the wind erosion equation. When rye strips are included in a plasticulture system, each strip reduces the wind run and lessens the wind velocity.

General Design Criteria for Successful Windbreaks

- The optimal cross-sectional shape of a windbreak has vertical rather than sloping sides.
- The optimal density for a windbreak is 40–60%.
- A windbreak should extend to the ground.
- The width of windbreaks has a negligible effect

on protection, except as it affects penetrability. Generally, a 40–60% density is preferred as a good compromise between distance protected leeward and land used by the windbreak. A single row of rye may provide this or a single row of snow fencing. More individual rows may be required depending on the plant species and in-row spacing. For perennial (tree or shrub) windbreaks, multiple rows are planted with the plants staggered in the rows (offset from one row to the next) to achieve the desired density and level of protection as quickly as possible. For most plants, two to three rows are sufficient.

- The species height within a windbreak's width should be varied to create rough windbreak edges.
- The zone of protection created by a windbreak possessing the above characteristics extends leeward for a distance equal to 30 times the windbreak's height. Maximum protection is provided at a leeward distance of five to seven times the windbreak's height.
- Windbreaks work most efficiently when their length is 11.5 times greater than their mature height.

These general design rules, from *Landscape Design for Wind Control* by Pitt, Kissida, and Gould, are very appropriate for shelterbelt design and permanent windbreak plantings. The information is also good to know when planning and planting temporary or annual windbreaks.

Most research literature agrees that windbreaks can provide leeward protection for roughly ten times their height (10H) and windward protection for a smaller distance (1H–3H). The maximum wind reduction occurs in a zone 3H–6H leeward. The extent of the protection depends on the height and density of the windbreak. The density depends on the width of the barrier and the type of plant material used in the windbreak. For example, a tree windbreak composed of conifer species will be more dense than one composed of deciduous species.

Annual Windbreaks

Many different small-grain crops can be used for annual windbreaks in plasticulture production systems. The two main methods currently used are (1) planting strips of small grain between the rows after laying the plastic mulch or (2) planting the small grain and then later establishing the planting beds within the field of grain.

Strips of small grain, most often annual rye, are perhaps the most common method to provide wind protection for high-value crops such as melons, tomatoes, peppers, squash, and so forth, grown with or without plasticulture techniques (photo 6-1). The following example shows how to integrate small-grain windbreaks with plasticulture of melons.

Photo 6-1. Matured strips of annual rye every 30–40 feet across the field provide wind protection.

A general recommendation for windbreaks in a plasticulture system is to plant strips of annual rye every 30–40 feet across the field. The grain strips are usually 6–8 feet wide or at least the width of the tractor and equipment. Where climate allows, they should be established in the fall and planted at a time that allows successful germination and adequate fall and winter growth to ensure rapid growth in the spring. This will ensure that the grain gains the height needed for adequate wind protection when the crop emerges or is transplanted. If planting cool-season crops such as broccoli, you may want to plant the rye strips closer together to ensure adequate wind protection when the rye is shorter early in the season. Remember, the best wind protection is in the area within ten times the height of the windbreak.

Prepare the soil as for planting any small-grain crop. The seeding rate for the small grain should be comparable to that used when establishing a good cover crop, yet not so heavy as to cause lodging. For example, on the DelMarVa Peninsula, rye can be seeded at 80–110 pounds per acre in mid- to late September.

One advantage of rye is that it can be planted later in the fall than most other cover crops. Rye can establish in very cool weather and will germinate at temperatures as low as 34°F. Vegetative growth requires temperatures in the 40°F range.

Small-grain windbreak strips of cereal rye can eventually grow 5 feet tall. The strips can be mowed, chopped, rolled, or sprayed after the windiest part of the season has passed or left standing until harvest (photo 6-2). To prevent heading yet still provide some wind protection, some growers cut the rye back to about a 3-foot height of stems. Other growers even harvest the strips. Growers should do whatever works best for their individual operations.

Small-grain windbreaks also can help reduce erosion, suppress weeds, and act as a nutrient catch crop. One disadvantage is that temporary windbreak strips occupy 6–8 feet of field for every 20–40 feet across the field. If a grower has a wind-erosion problem, however, this disadvantage is negligible. Windbreaks reduce sandblasting that damages young plants and also reduce whipping and damaging of vines. Melons grow faster, because the temperature around the plant is higher due to shelter from the wind.

This small-grain windbreak system often produces melons one to two weeks earlier than melon production on bare ground without wind protection. Often total marketable yields of vine crops increase due to improved bee pollination of the protected crop. Com-

Photo 6-2. Rye windbreak mowed down and used as a drive row for harvesting or spraying the crop.

bining improved yields and earlier production, the pricing advantages gained help offset the land used for windbreaks. In addition, windbreak strips are often used as drive and spray roads later in the season, which reduces plant damage since equipment is not driven over the vines.

An alternative to using rye windbreaks every 30–40 feet across a field is to use rye or another small grain as in-row protective strips. In this technique, a cover crop is fall-drilled over the entire field or small strips are seeded on 5- to 6-foot centers. Instead of plowing the field in the spring, an agricultural rototiller is used to till strips through the cover crop. One or two plastic-covered raised beds are formed in this tilled swath. A strip of grain approximately 20 inches wide is left between the beds or between the group of two beds. The rye or small-grain mini-strip is allowed to grow. Once this mini-strip reaches the desired height, it is killed with a selective grass herbicide or, using a shielded sprayer, a nonresidual herbicide for general vegetation control, such as glyphosate or paraquat. The mini-strip vegetation is eventually tilled into the soil middles, mowed, or left to protect the exposed soil surface. Tillage or mowing must be accomplished before the crop extends beyond the plastic mulch.

Strawberry production in a plasticulture system provides an example of one way to incorporate an annual small-grain windbreak with a transplanted crop. The site selected should have a wooded area or windbreak to protect the strawberry planting from prevailing winds. However, air movement through the site must be sufficient to dry plants quickly after dew or rainfall to minimize the potential for fungus disease. To further protect this high-value, tender crop from wind and water erosion, the row middles can be overseeded with annual rye grass. This is done after the raised plastic beds are made but before the holes are punched in the plastic to plant the strawberries. An overhead irrigation system can be used to wash seeds off the plastic and to help get the rye established. In the late winter, the rye grass can be controlled with a labeled contact grass herbicide, or the middles can be sprayed with a shielded sprayer applying a nonselective herbicide such as paraquat or glyphosate. Spraying must be done carefully, following all label precautions.

The benefits in reduced wind and soil abrasion to the strawberry crop, especially early in the season, are significant. However, one precaution is necessary. A number of growers and specialists have observed that, when living mulches are used in row middles between the raised plastic mulch in plasticulture strawberry production, there can be a loss of a degree or two in frost protection versus a bare-soil row middle. There are two reasons for this: one, if the mulch is killed and covered by a heavy residue, the soil will not warm as quickly and two, if the living mulch is not killed soon enough, it can deplete soil moisture. In each case, as the temperature drops, there is less latent heat held in the soil moisture to radiate back to the surrounding plants.

Perennial or Permanent Windbreaks

Hardwood and pine woodlands provide wind protection if they are perpendicular to the direction of the wind. Permanent windbreaks can also be established with a wide range of perennial plants, including native or horticultural trees, shrubs, and tall perennial grasses (photo 6-3). The major advantage of establishing a perennial windbreak is that they are higher and last longer. With protection on both the leeward and windward sides of a windbreak, the sheltered zone between two parallel windbreaks can extend for 300 to 500 feet or more. While it may take 10 to 20 years for a tree windbreak to reach its mature height, most tree windbreaks have a life span of more than 50 years. The real plus is that once they are established, they

Photo 6-3. Permanent tree windbreaks provide wind protection.

can provide protection throughout the year for a number of years.

A wide range of species are appropriate for use in perennial windbreaks. In their Maryland Cooperative Extension leaflet, "Plants for Windbreaks" (now out of print), Kissida, Pitt, and Gould discuss the materials and advice below.

Evergreen trees are the foundation of windbreaks. Their year-round, dense foliage and branches extend to the ground and provide a greater amount of protection during the winter than deciduous trees. Therefore, evergreen trees should be included in all windbreaks wherever possible.

Shrubs are commonly planted along the windward edge of a windbreak to increase its density. They also provide ideal low windbreaks and frequently serve as living snow fences. In many areas, shrub rows provide newly planted evergreens with protection while the trees are getting established.

In selecting plants for use in windbreaks, it is important to consider wind tolerance along with other factors. Each species will have advantages and disadvantages in any given situation. For example, in Maryland, eastern red cedar, Canada hemlock, loblolly pine, and arborvitae are not recommended. Although these plants would appear to be suitable at first glance, they are not included for the following reasons:

- Eastern red cedar is the alternate host for cedar-apple rust, a serious disease of apples and crabapples.
- Canada hemlock is easily desiccated by continued exposure to cold winter winds.
- Loblolly pine, used extensively on the eastern shore, loses its lower branches early in its growth cycle, making it a poor choice.
- Arborvitae has dense foliage, but its wood is weak and stems break under heavy snow or ice.

Some of the trees suggested for use in windbreaks (and their limitations) are listed below:

Leland cypress *(Cupressocyparis leylandii)*. Mature height is 80–100 feet. This fast-growing, extremely vigorous tree is narrowly pyramidal (almost columnar) with very compact, flattened branchlets. It will grow in a variety of soils. Its columnar habit makes it hard to blend into the landscape. It is very tolerant of seashore locations and free of disease and insect pests. Ice storms can cause damage.

Norway spruce *(Picea abies)*. Mature height is up to 90 feet. This medium-fast-growing, dark green, dense, pyramidal tree has graceful, pendulous branches. It likes moist, fertile soil. It is susceptible to spruce gall, aphid damage, and spider mites.

White spruce *(Picea glauca)*. Mature height is up to 90 feet. This medium-fast-growing native tree has a pyramidal habit with light bluish green needles. It can endure heat and drought better than most spruces and is very hardy. Several other spruces are more ornamental. It is susceptible to spruce gall, aphid damage, and spider mites.

White pine *(Pinus strobus)*. Height is up to 150 feet. This very fast-growing, dense, rounded to pyramidal tree has soft, flexible, and delicate green needles. Drooping needles give it a graceful appearance; it is picturesque when old. White pine is susceptible to white pine weevil and white pine blister rust but is otherwise free of insect pests and diseases.

Scots pine *(Pinus sylvestris)*. Mature height is up to 75 feet. This medium-fast-growing, open, round-topped tree has an irregular habit of growth. It is valued for its bluish green foliage and picturesque, open habit at maturity. It has coarse, reddish brown bark and large branches. It is susceptible to Nantucket pine tip moth when young and girdling by mice but is otherwise free of pests and diseases.

Douglas fir *(Pseudotsuga menziesii)*. Mature height is 80–150 feet (300 feet or more on the West Coast). This medium-fast-growing tree has a densely pyramidal shape with bluish green needlelike foliage. It is readily distinguished from all other evergreens by its unique pendulous cones and very soft needles. It is considered one of the best native evergreen ornamentals. It is susceptible to bagworm and white mealy bug injury, which can be easily controlled. This tree does not do well where temperatures remain high for long periods.

Eastern red cedar *(Juniperus virginiana).* Mature height is 25–30 feet for use as screen or hedge. A native evergreen, it is naturally upright and requires very little trimming. Plant trees about 4–6 feet apart in a row. It is a problem host for cedar apple rust and bag worms and is slow-growing.

Single and double rows of windbreaks are the normal recommendation. A double row usually consists of a row of trees with shrubs or slow-growing conifers on the windward side of the break. To ensure a good stand and offer early protection, plant trees at a closer spacing, but thin or remove them to the recommended spacing once they begin to close in. It may seem like permanent windbreaks take up a lot of land, but if a 1,000-foot-long windbreak occupies 10 feet between rows or even a width of 20 feet when mature, it occupies less than one-half acre and provides wind-control benefits for more than 7 acres.

Each piece of ground is different, so be familiar with the plant hardiness zones for your area. Select a species or mix of species that will do well in your area and in the particular soil and moisture conditions in your fields. Species that have few serious pest problems are best. Do not use any plant material that could become a pest problem, such as the multiflora rose or autumn olive. Select species for a perennial windbreak carefully to make sure your windbreak planting is off to a good start. Your local Cooperative Extension office, Natural Resources Conservative Service (NRCS) office, or local forester can recommend planting materials appropriate for your area. It is highly recommended that you discuss your situation with these resource agencies. They will also know about any federal or state programs developed to encourage the establishment of perennial windbreaks to reduce soil erosion.

The three major drawbacks to establishing a permanent perennial windbreak are (1) the cost of establishment and maintenance, (2) the time required to reach the desired mature height, and (3) the competition in the shadow zone or root zone of the adjacent crop. While these need to be considered, it should be remembered that a permanent windbreak is a long-term investment for both the benefit of the crop and the environment. As with many naturally occurring woodlands among crop fields, the area immediately adjacent to the trees or shrubs can be used for roads to provide access to the field. Brandle et al. (1992) stated that with as little as 1–5% of the land base devoted to windbreaks, a producer can protect a crop, improve yield and quality, and increase profitability.

Fencing and Other Web-Type Windbreaks

Wooden-slat or snow fencing can be used as a temporary windbreak. Its use is limited because it is commonly only 4 feet high. It is most often used on very small production areas or for temporary protection. When land is very limited, this type of artificial wind protection may be appropriate and cost-effective, as it can be used for more than one season.

The newer plastic snow fencing such as the Paraweb design fencing may be even more practical than wood fencing. Paraweb windbreaks are being used in a number of countries, most notably New Zealand. These artificial web windbreaks are quite commonly used on high-value crops and have been quite successful. They are designed to be approximately 46% permeable, thus permitting air to pass through, reducing turbulence, and giving good wind reduction over a large area. The plastic or nylon web is securely strung between posts.

A number of manufacturers exist for these products. They are expensive but take up little space and are quick to set up. A further advantage of the web artificial windbreak materials is they do not deplete soil moisture or soil nutrients from nearby crops. Such products usually have a reasonably long life, but repair and replacement costs need to be considered.

Other Methods for Reducing Wind-Related Problems

Organic or Natural Mulches

Covering the row middles with organic or other natural mulches can greatly reduce the effect of sand or soil movement but will not reduce the force of the wind as effectively as annual in-row grain windbreaks or permanent perennial windbreaks. The row middles can be mulched with straw, such as pine straw, small-grain straw, or chopped switchgrass, or similar materials. One major drawback is the cost and expense of applying the mulches with only limited protection provided in return.

Irrigation

This preventive technique keeps the top layer of soil from drying out. As the soil dries—especially a sandy or muck soil—wind blowing along the soil surface in the 15-mile-per-hour range will cause the soil particles to begin moving. The drier the soil becomes, the more the particles move. By irrigating the soil and keeping it wet, the amount of soil movement can be reduced. Here again, this technique is costly and only a temporary solution. Plants are still subject to wind and its adverse effects. This technique will only temporarily minimize the abrasion caused by moving soil.

Strip Tilling

In strip tilling, different crops or mixes of crops are planted in the field. Instead of having one large open field planted to one crop, there are strips of several different crops, often with different heights and growth characteristics. The uneven surface topography of the field slows wind velocity. This technique is not as effective as other forms of windbreaks and may not be practical for a medium- or large-scale operation.

Summary

Wind management is critical to the successful production of high-value crops such as vegetables, strawberries, and cut flowers. The establishment of annual and/or permanent windbreaks must be recognized as a good horticultural practice that involves fertility, water management, weed control, pest control, required maintenance, and management.

When planning a windbreak, keep these thoughts in mind:

- What is the direction of the prevailing winds during the critical windy period, February through June?
- When the wind reaches a velocity approaching 15 miles per hour, soil particles will be moving with potential for abrasion injuries to leaves and fruit.
- When wind velocity exceeds approximately 9 miles per hour, most vegetables respond with physiological changes that result in reduced yields and lower quality.
- A windbreak provides a shelter distance up to 10 times the height of the barrier.
- The barrier should allow for some air movement though it; windbreaks with densities of 40–60% provide the greatest combined benefits of wind reduction and protection.

Brandle et al. very aptly stated, "Windbreaks reduce wind speed and improve the microclimate in sheltered zones. They provide many direct benefits to the producer while maximizing the ecological benefits of ecosystem diversity. They should be an integral part of all vegetable production systems, including plasticulture. While effects of high wind speeds and soil abrasion are quickly evident, other less obvious reductions in yield and crop quality can result from wind stress at relatively low wind speeds. Wind protection systems, either artificial or vegetative, permanent or seasonal, offer benefits in improved microclimate for plant growth. Windbreaks enhance soil warming and improve the water-use-efficiency characteristic of plasticulture. A better understanding of how shelter modifies crop growth will allow design of wind protection systems that achieve the desired modification in microclimate and plant growth, while reducing the expense of windbreak establishment."

CHAPTER 7

Crop Establishment Options, Machinery, and Spacings for Plasticulture

Michael D. Orzolek

P lasticulture systems enable growers to optimize establishment of vegetable and fruit crops under less-than-optimum conditions and in locations with short growing seasons. Generally, warm-season crops such as muskmelon, pepper, tomato, and so forth, are established from transplants to decrease the time to maturity in the field. Direct-seeding of vegetables such as sweet corn, cucumber, and snap bean through plastic allows for optimum soil temperature and moisture conditions to ensure maximum seed germination and subsequent seedling emergence. Mechanization of transplanting or seeding of vegetables in plasticulture is available and successful if the beds are firm and flat with plastic film firmly stretched over them and if specific crop requirements are followed during crop establishment.

Vegetable crop production in the Northeast and mid-Atlantic states in the early 1950s was thought to be limited by extremes in temperature and moisture. The early efforts of Dr. Emery M. Emmert at the University of Kentucky (Jones 1994) demonstrated that plastic film, whether it was applied to the soil or covered a stationery structure, dramatically improved crop yields by helping to maintain more favorable soil temperatures and moisture levels. Since that early research by Emmert, plasticulture development for vegetable production has included raised beds, drip irrigation, plastic mulch, low hoop-supported plastic tunnels/row covers, and high walk-in tunnels. All of these plasticulture components contribute to the optimization of climatic factors while reducing environmental stress. Proper plant establishment—either by seeds or transplants—is critical to achieving maximum benefits from plasticulture. Whether to use seeds or transplants depends on several factors.

Plant Establishment

The optimization of crop production is entirely dependent on successful stand establishment (Orzolek 1991). The big difference between conventional culture and plasticulture is that the area can be controlled or modified, starting with initial establishment. The microclimate surrounding the plant, including soil temperature, soil moisture, relative humidity, and air temperature above the plastic film, is generally best for plant establishment when there are minimal extremes in fluctuation in a 24-hour cycle. Establishing vegetable transplants or seeds can be more difficult in a conservation tillage system because of the lower and more variable soil temperature and moisture levels.

Generally, warm-season crops such as muskmelon, watermelon, summer squash, cucumber, tomato, pepper, eggplant, okra, and sweet corn respond with greater plant growth and higher marketable yields in plasticulture systems. Depending on the planting date, the growth and yield response of cool-season crops to plasticulture has not been consistent compared to the warm-season crop response.

A primary challenge in establishing vegetables in plastic mulch is how to perforate the plastic so that seeds or transplants can be placed in the soil (Shaw 1987). Plastic can be perforated in several ways; it can be pierced with a sharp edge, punched with a blunt tip, and melted with a propane burner. No single perforation method works for all establishment techniques. Which method to use depends on the method of establishment, equipment availability, labor requirement, and cost. If using transplants, the plug size will often determine the size of hole needed and therefore the most efficient perforation method.

The ability to perforate the plastic mulch also depends on how tight the plastic film is stretched over the bed and the firmness of the soil in the bed. If the plastic film does not fit the bed tightly or the soil is loose and collapses in the bed, then it will be difficult to cleanly puncture the plastic film. Other concerns related to perforating the plastic film are that the holes can act as funnels and direct hot air onto the young transplants; potential for germination of weed seeds can increase; and damage can occur from mice and birds.

Transplanting

Using transplants in plasticulture enables growers to extend the season, double- or triple-crop on plastic mulch, avoid extremes of temperature and moisture, and reduce crop-production costs (Shaw et al. 1978). The two types of transplants available to commercial growers are bare-root and plug or tray plants. Bare-root transplants are directly seeded in the field at generally high populations and harvested when the plants have reached the optimum transplant age for individual crops. Plug or tray plants are grown in greenhouses or high tunnels in Styrofoam or plastic trays with specific cell sizes (0.5- to 4.0-inch squares) prior to transplanting in the field at a specific transplant age (photo 7-1). It may be necessary to establish a crop from transplants to increase the percentage of early-harvested fruit (Ng and Schales 1978) or reduce the time to harvest of a crop where the number of frost-free growing days is less than 120. Transplants also enable growers to produce long-maturing crops such as eggplant in the field in the Northeast. Okra trans-

Photo 7-1. Container-grown tomato transplants.

plants have been used during soil solarization in the South to generate income in a late-season postplant solarization system (Khan et al. 1993). (See chapter 9 for more information on solarization.) Several important factors determine the success or failure of transplanting in a plasticulture system.

Transplant quality is one key to successful establishment. Actively growing plants that are disease- and insect-free are more stress-resistant and acclimate faster to environmental conditions when placed in the field. Hardened-off, old, or pest-infected plants often have high rates of mortality, even in the production greenhouse. Transplants are often placed in a harsh environment with extremes in temperature and moisture fluctuation, continual desiccation from wind, and early stress from insects and diseases. Unless these plants receive inputs that diminish the effects of these environmental stresses, plant mortality is inevitable. Applying water, fertilizer, or both through a drip system immediately after transplanting and using row covers, low tunnels, or windbreaks can mitigate the effects of the environment.

Other problems become evident even after plants become successfully established. A common problem found in the field after successful crop establishment is stem injury or desiccation of transplants (such as pepper) when hot air moves under loose plastic and is funneled through the perforated hole of each plant. It is crucial to have a very tight fit of the plastic over raised beds. Since most mulch colors dramatically raise soil temperature, tender transplants can be burned by direct contact with the plastic film. Transplants should be centered in the holes, and the holes should be round, evenly cut, and sufficiently large so that the plastic does not come in contact with the plant. Uniform plant depth is also important for plant establishment, uniformity of plant development during the growing season, and a uniform harvest. Plants planted too deeply may develop root diseases within weeks after transplanting. Shallow plantings can result in lodging and plants that are more sensitive to moisture stress.

Crops

Using transplants in plasticulture generally results in earlier harvests if plants are growing actively when transplanted, more complete and uniform stands, and more options for pest management (Wilson et al. 1993). Generally, warm-season crops are transplanted in plasticulture systems, including tomato, pepper, eggplant, okra, muskmelon, watermelon, slicing cucumber, summer squash, and pumpkins. For extremely early corn in the Northeast, a small but significant percentage of corn acreage is transplanted in plasticulture, reducing time to maturity by a minimum of seven to ten days. The age of the sweet corn transplant is very important, and the greatest success of sweet corn establishment has been with 17- to 21-day-old transplants. In southern states (below Virginia), pepper transplants set to the depth of the cotyledon leaves or the first true leaf reduces heat stress on roots and minimizes fluctuations in soil temperature (Vavrina et al. 1994). In northern climates, setting pepper transplants deep in plasticulture does not produce the same response (Orzolek, unpublished data). Several other crops such as lettuce, broccoli, cauliflower, onion, and winter squash can be established as transplants if earliness and reduction in environmental stress are required. Marr and Lamont (1990) suggested the use of asparagus transplants in plasticulture for establishment of this perennial crop with the advantage of potentially earlier and higher spear production.

Container Cell Size

The cell size of the flat used for transplant production can have a direct effect on transplant growth but not on marketable crop yield after establishment in the field. Fisher and Julian (1988) found no difference in total fruit yield from tomato transplants grown in either 400- or 200-cell trays (although there was a visible difference in plant size from plants grown in the two cell sizes). Tomato transplants had a higher number of leaves, greater leaf area, larger stems, and higher dry weight when grown in 338-cell (80 A) trays (manufactured by Speedling Corporation) compared to the 200-cell trays (Beverly et al. 1992, Bennett and Grassbaugh 1992). However, Garton (1992) found that tomato transplants produced in 406-cell trays (manufactured by TLC Polyform) performed just as well as the larger standard 288-cell trays if established under optimum growing conditions (plasticulture). There was no difference in growth and yield of pepper transplants

grown in three different cell sizes (200-cell tray manufactured by Speedling, 200-cell tray manufactured by Landmark Plastics Corporation, and 288-cell tray manufactured by Landmark) seven weeks after transplanting, but there were differences in early pepper transplant growth in the field after transplanting that did not carry through to harvest (Bennett and Grassbaugh 1995). However, smaller cell sizes are much more economical compared to large cell sizes (Olson 1999).

Transplant Age

The age of vegetable transplants depends on the crop, variety (cultivar), climate, vigor, and stress tolerance of the transplant. A wide range of plant ages will produce acceptable crop yields, provided that the plant has not become totally reproductive (with both flowers and immature fruit) at the time of transplanting into the field. In tomato, for example, transplants from two to 13 weeks of age have been established successfully in the field and have produced very acceptable yields; however, the optimum physiological plant age at transplanting for tomato is four to seven weeks (Vavrina and Orzolek 1993). NeSmith (1994) reported that the transplant age of muskmelon had a significant effect on growth and development of 2-, 4-, 6-, and 8-week-old transplants but had no significant effect on early and total fruit yields. In fact, the 6- and 8-week-old muskmelon transplants began to flower prior to transplanting in both years. Similar results were obtained with summer squash. Ten- to 35-day-old squash transplants produced similar yields but had different growth rates; younger transplants (10–21 days) grew faster than 28- to 35-day-old transplants (NeSmith 1992). The recommended age for summer squash transplants is 21 days, since this would allow for an additional 10-day delay in planting before yield reduction would occur.

Starter Solution

The use of high-phosphorus starter solutions in plasticulture depends on the soil temperature at transplanting and the length of time after transplanting that phosphorus will be applied through the drip irrigation system. Research on use of starter solutions has been extensive over the last 50 years, but there has been no agreement among researchers on crop response and efficacy. Since the cost of applying a 10-52-10, 12-48-8, or similar-analysis fertilizer is relatively low ($7.00–$10.00 per acre), growers have used high-phosphorus starter solutions applied either at transplant time or through the drip irrigation tape as insurance against early phosphorus deficiency symptoms appearing on their crops. The use of tray-grown transplants that were grown under a pretransplant nutritional conditioning system has all but eliminated phosphorus deficiency in most crops after transplanting in the field.

Application of a starter solution is no substitute for a soil test. Annual soil tests in an active crop rotation system are critical. They report actual elemental amounts of phosphorus, potassium, calcium, and magnesium in the soil and include recommendations for the crop to be grown based on the current soil content of those elements.

Mechanization

Manual transplanting on a large scale in plasticulture systems is labor-intensive, time-consuming, and inconsistent compared to mechanical transplanting. The variability in transplant depth during manual transplanting results in nonuniform crop establishment and growth in the field, and in some instances results in high transplant mortality. Several transplanting machines on the market place plants through the perforated plastic mechanically but require manual setting of plants into fingers or carousels. Only two or three fully automated transplanting systems are in use around the world. None is currently manufactured or available in the United States (Shaw 1988). The automated mechanical transplanters are expensive, but they require only a tractor driver. Manual transplanters, on the other hand, require a tractor driver plus two to eight people to place transplants in the planter or through the plastic and firm soil around the plants. In addition, automated transplanters have a high capacity for transplanting in the field (3,000–4,000 plants per hour per acre).

Many models of transplanters have a large tank for water or starter solution, which is applied simultaneously with or immediately after setting the transplants in the soil. In addition, a wide range of plant sizes can be placed in the field, depending on the feeding mechanism of the transplanter (fingers, clamshells,

or a carousel with drop tube). There are several limitations with these planters. They cannot plant closer than 12 inches in the row, there is a limited range of tractor operating speeds (thus limiting total transplant volume per day), and it is difficult to transplant under wet soil conditions. See appendix A, page 123, for a list of companies that manufacture or distribute different types of transplanters. Photos 7-2 through 7-5 show some of the different types of available transplanters.

Direct-Seeding

Crops

Because high soil temperatures and moisture levels are required for optimum crop production with direct-seeding of sweet corn, cucumber, summer squash, and melon, early production is more feasible in northern climates using plasticulture (photo 7-6). Since the planting date is 7–14 days earlier than planting dates with nonplasticulture systems, conditions following seedling emergence are very critical, since minimum air temperatures can fall below optimum threshold temperatures for active growth. Other vegetable crops that can be sown directly in plastic are snap bean, onion, lettuce, and broccoli. Using primed seeds may be more effective in plasticulture because of the more

Photo 7-2. Transplanter from MAS Manufacturing in Candiana, Italy, which will lay paper/plastic degradable mulch on the soil and transplant through the paper/plastic in one operation.

Photo 7-6. Some crops such as sweet corn, cucumbers, summer squash, and melons, can be successfully direct-seeded through the plastic mulch.

Photos 7-3 and 7-4. Standard water-wheel transplanter available from several equipment manufacturers throughout the United States with adjustable spacing between wheels and wheels with different in-row spacings.

Photo 7-5. Transplanter from Checchi & Magli, Italy, that uses pockets to accept transplants and then places them in the soil through the plastic film. This transplanter is available from BDI Machinery Sales, Macungie, Pennsylvania.

favorable temperature and moisture conditions for seed germination and seedling growth. Successful direct-seeding of vegetable crops in plasticulture is more predictable if the location generally has a long growing season. One report indicated that plug-transplanted melon crops produced a significantly higher marketable fruit yield than direct-seeded melons in plasticulture (Brown 1991).

Plant Population

The final plant population of any vegetable crop seeded in plastic mulch is determined by the spacing in the row, number of rows per bed, and center-to-center spacing between beds. There are some physical restrictions when seeding the crop that limit spacing options, including the location and placement of the drip irrigation tape in the bed, type of seeding unit available, type of spray application equipment used in the field, and size and growth habit of the planted crop.

If drip tape is placed in the center of the bed, then at least two rows can be planted on the bed. If the tape is placed on one side of the bed, then only one row can be planted on the bed. The deeper the drip tape is placed in the bed (2–3 inches), the more precise the location of the tape will be in the finished bed. It is easier to plant multiple rows of a crop on the bed if tape location is predictable.

In some cases, because of the physical size of the planter, only one unit can be used behind the tractor to plant a single row. If the unit is off-centered, two rows can be planted with a double pass over the bed. Between-row spacings may be limited, depending on the type of sprayer used in making pesticide applications (boom or airblast). Finally, some plants require more space per unit area than others because of size and/or growth habit (think eggplant versus cucumber). Typical plant spacings for direct-seeded or transplanted vegetables are given in table 7-1.

Double-Cropping

Because plasticulture reduces the time to crop maturity, many locations in the United States are able to produce two crops per season on nondegradable, high-quality plastic mulch. Direct-seeding facilitates the planting and emergence of many crops under optimum soil temperatures, and growth is predictable under specific temperature regimes in the field.

Double-cropping allows a grower to harvest a crop in a high market window, remove plant debris from existing mulch rows, and then plant a second crop in the mulch, usually by perforating new holes in the plastic and placing the seed in the soil. It is important to keep in mind some of the basics of integrated pest management, namely, crop rotation, sanitation before planting the second crop, and maintenance of pest-free conditions for the first 30 days after planting, to enhance crop establishment and early crop development. Knowing the approximate number of days for optimum plant growth (the growing season) will help growers define crops to be grown for double-cropping

TABLE 7-1

Plant spacing for field production with plasticulture

CROP	IN-ROW SPACING (inches) Single row	Double row	BETWEEN-ROW SPACING (inches) ON PLASTIC MULCH
Common on plastic			
Cucumber (slicers)	12–18	9–18	12–14
Cucumber (pickles)	12–18	9–18	12–14
Eggplant	18–24	18–30	14–16
Honeydew	18–24	____	____
Lettuce (leaf)	8–12	10–14	12–14
Muskmelon	18–24	____	____
Okra	12–18	18	14–16
Pepper	12–16	12–16	12–14
Pumpkin	24–48	____	____
Summer squash	12–18	16–24	14–16
Winter squash	18–24	____	____
Tomato	18–24	____	____
Less common on plastic[1]			
Broccoli	____	8–12	9–12
Cabbage	____	9–12	12–16
Cauliflower	18	18–24	14–18
Chinese cabbage	12	12–14	12–14
Collard	9–12	12–18	12–18
Potato	8–12	12	16–18
Sweet corn	6	6–12	12–18
Sweet potato	12	____	____
Leafy greens	____	6–12	9–12 (2–3 rows)
Onion	____	4–6	4–10 (3–6 rows)

[1] Used in double- or triple-cropping

and the economic viability of the market window. Some recommendations include growing snap bean after cucumber, broccoli after melon, and summer squash after early sweet corn—especially in more southern locations in the United States. Cleaning the plant debris off the mulch from the first crop is important to ensure successful establishment of the second crop, reduce physical interference during seeding, reduce pest populations, and ensure the breakdown of plant debris. The first crop can be removed either mechanically (with a mower, flail chopper, or other machine) or chemically (with contact or nonselective herbicides).

Mechanization

The use of specialized seeders is critical for successful establishment of a seeded vegetable crop on plastic mulch (Orzolek and Daum 1984). To date, most of the planters developed for planting vegetable seeds through plastic mulch have a metal dibble that pierces a hole in the plastic mulch and places an individual seed in the hole. Several types of seed-dispensing mechanisms are available with different planters, but singulation with a precision seeder has been the basic unit for seeding vegetables on plastic-covered raised beds (Orzolek and Daum 1986, Inman 1995).

An early machine developed to direct-seed vegetables in plastic mulch was a plug-mix planter. With this planter, vegetable seed was mixed in specific ratios with a peat/perlite soilless medium to achieve a specific plant population per acre and a specific number of seeds per hole when the mix was deposited in each perforation (Hayslip 1973). A propane burner was used to burn teardrop-shaped openings in the plastic. This method was successful as long as there was enough moisture in the peat/perlite mixture to sustain seed germination and emergence.

One planter currently used to direct-seed vegetables on plastic mulch is the Poly Planter from Ferris Farms in New Wilmington, Pennsylvania. This planter uses a metal dibble to perforate the plastic mulch while singulating seeds in each perforated hole at a uniform depth. Seed spacing is variable both within and between rows, so a large range of plant populations are obtainable. See appendix A, page 123, for contact information for Ferris Farms. Photos 7-7 and 7-8 show one type of direct-seeder that is currently available.

Most Common Mistakes Made during Plant Establishment in Plasticulture

1. Lack of a firm, uniformly level bed can create air pockets between soil and plastic mulch. If air flows underneath mulch, hot air can funnel through the perforated holes of the plastic, resulting in stem damage to plants. Produce a firm, level, continuous bed to prevent this problem.

2. Loose plastic mulch over a raised bed can result in plant desiccation or death if transplants become covered with the loose plastic. In addition, wind can lift the plastic mulch off the beds. To prevent this prob-

Photos 7-7 and 7-8. Monosem planter, which will direct-seed various vegetable crops through plastic mulch by use of propane gas to burn a hole in the plastic film prior to the seed being placed in the soil. Available from several machinery dealers in the United States.

lem, before laying film in the field, adjust the plastic mulch applicator to place the mulch film tightly over the beds.

3. Poorly placed drip irrigation tape in the raised bed can result in nonuniform soil moisture levels and nutrient application. If the drip tape is not placed beneath the soil surface in a perfectly straight line, it will be difficult to transplant without puncturing the tape. Using a drip tape applicator with a hollow chisel placed at a 2- to 3-inch depth in the bed will prevent this problem.

4. Failure to operate the drip irrigation system immediately after transplanting—especially if soil moisture is less than 60% of capacity—will result in poor establishment or desiccation of the transplants. Drip irrigation systems should be installed and operational before transplanting to prevent this problem. In addition, as plants increase in size, soil-moisture-sensing probes such as tensiometers should be used to help maintain optimum soil moisture and determine when and how long drip irrigation systems should be operated.

5. Failure to remove floating row covers or plastic tunnels from a developing crop can result in plant damage or death from excessive heat. Placing thermometers under row cover or tunnels in several locations, taking frequent readings, and recording air temperatures will help prevent this problem.

6. Failure to either calibrate the fertilizer injector or calculate correctly fertilizer rates can result in early seedling/plant damage from excessive salt levels. Calibrate fertilizer injectors with known concentrations of nitrogen, phosphorus, and potassium prior to transplanting to verify that the injector is working correctly. In addition, have a Cooperative Extension agent or irrigation company representative review calculations of fertilizer concentrations to prevent this problem.

7. Failure to remove floating row covers or plastic tunnels from a cucurbit crop during flower anthesis will result in poor fruit pollination. Monitor fields of cucurbit crops for flower development at least once a week to help prevent this problem.

CHAPTER 8

Weed Management in Plasticulture

A. Richard Bonanno

When producing vegetable crops in field plasticulture, good weed management is as essential as in a bare-ground management system. However, weed management strategies are more complex in plasticulture. Fewer chemical options exist, cultivation is difficult, and there is greater potential for crop injury. This chapter describes the differences in weed management that must be addressed when plasticulture is added to the production cycle. Three specific areas will be discussed: weed management under plastic mulch, weed management between plastic mulch, and weed management under row covers.

Weed Management under Plastic Mulch

Soil fumigation is sometimes used under plastic mulches. While it is used primarily for disease and nematode control, weed management is also a benefit. However, not all weeds are controlled by soil fumigation, and generally metham-sodium is not as effective as methyl bromide in providing good weed control. The ongoing phasing out of methyl bromide in the United States and elsewhere will limit choices to metham-sodium and metham-sodium-like products.

To obtain good control of weed seeds, rhizomes, and tubers under the mulch, soil conditions must be favorable. Specifically, soil temperatures should be at least 60°F, soil moisture should be near field capacity, and seeds and tubers should not be dormant.

Two weed types that commonly escape soil fumigation are nutsedge (*Cyperus* species) and legumes (such as clover and vetch). Nutsedge tubers are usually dormant in the early spring, when soil temperatures may be suitable for treatment. Ideally, a summer or fall application is best for controlling nutsedge tubers with fumigation. Legume seeds are seldom killed by soil fumigation. Legume seed coats are very hard; fumigation scarifies these seeds and may actually improve their germination.

When fumigants are placed under plastic mulches, the waiting period before planting is usually extended up to four weeks. This is because the plastic slows the loss of vapors and prevents the ability to work the soil to expedite the loss. Methyl bromide evaporates from the soil in about two weeks or less. Metham-sodium, however, can take up to four weeks to dissipate. As a result, it is best used as a summer or fall treatment. With fall planting in southern areas, waiting times can be much less. In northern areas of the United States, fall application (before the soil temperature drops below 50°F) combined with spring planting works best for metham-sodium.

Solarization may also be an option in some areas. Usually, a summer fallow is necessary to obtain proper temperatures. This technique is more common in southern areas of the United States. See chapter 9 for more information on solarization.

It is advisable to ensure that the fumigant has fully dissipated prior to planting. The "lettuce test" is the most common method. Treated soil and lettuce seed are placed into a sealed glass container with adequate moisture. If the lettuce germinates and does not turn brown, the fumigant has adequately dissipated.

Currently, metham-sodium is registered for use regardless of the crop that will be planted. Methyl bromide is registered for use only on the following field-produced vegetable crops: asparagus, broccoli, muskmelon, cauliflower, eggplant, lettuce, dry bulb onion, pepper, tomato, and strawberry. It can also be used on nonfood crops such as field-grown flowers. Note that methyl bromide may be applied to plant beds that are used to produce transplants of any crop. The key to the methyl bromide transplant registration is that the plants will be transplanted to a nontreated area.

If fumigation is applied under plastic strips, there is generally no need for an herbicide under the plastic. Under black plastic, herbicides are usually unnecessary regardless of fumigation. Nutsedge may be the exception, because it can sprout under black plastic and grow through it. Herbicides are usually needed under clear or white plastic if the soil is not fumigated. Colored mulches (including infrared-transmitting, IRT, types) have been used to mimic the soil-warming feature of clear plastic while providing the weed suppression of black plastic. In general, however, weeds are not adequately suppressed, although IRT mulches can suppress nutsedge. Local experience with colored plastics and IRT types will determine the need for herbicides.

With all plastics, weeds will likely grow in the planting holes. The question arises as to how competitive these weeds are and whether they interfere with the crop. Research has shown that differences among crops do exist. In results from North Carolina, transplanted tomato yields were not affected by weed growth in planting holes, muskmelon yields were 40% lower, and pepper yields were 73% lower when no herbicide was applied under black plastic (Monaco and Bonanno 1986). Yield losses appeared to be related to the speed of crop growth and the time required to achieve soil shading. Tomatoes grow vigorously after transplanting, whereas peppers grow very slowly the first two to three weeks after transplanting. Direct-seeded crops have little competitive advantage over the weeds, as crop emergence is similar in timing to weed emergence; therefore, a seeded crop would probably suffer greater yield loss than transplanted crops. Generally, weed growth in the plant holes will require either hand removal or an herbicide or fumigation treatment under the plastic.

Even in cases where weed growth in the plant holes may not influence yields, other factors should be considered. These include production of weed seeds, which can increase competition the following year, and interference with crop harvest. Therefore, the decision to use an herbicide under black plastic should be based primarily on the potential for crop competition with weeds in the planting holes.

The following suggestions will help optimize weed control under plastic:

1. Prepare a raised bed or use normal soil preparation if raised beds are not used.

2. Apply herbicide to the bed or soil surface.

3. Activate preemergence herbicides with rainfall or overhead irrigation (at least 0.5 inch), or incorporate the herbicide (if required) and reshape the bed. Herbicides applied under plastic mulch may be activated by condensation if good soil moisture is present when the mulch is applied, particularly when the soil is coarse and low in organic matter.

Incorporation of herbicides on raised beds is not always an easy task. Equipment modifications or specialized equipment may be required so that the herbicide is incorporated at the correct depth and the bed is not completely destroyed. Successful incorporation tools for beds include narrow rototiller units or rolling cultivators run in tandem over the beds.

Some growers have tried to incorporate herbicides on flat ground and then make raised beds. This practice may cause crop stunting by mixing the herbicide too deeply into the soil. When the bed is made after incorporation, soil is thrown from the aisles to the bed center. This results in treated soil being thrown on top of treated soil. An herbicide that was intended to be incorporated to a depth of 4 inches can easily end up 6–8 inches deep on a raised bed. When the crop is seeded or transplanted, the crop roots encounter the herbicide to a greater depth than is recommended, often resulting in crop stunting.

4. Apply the plastic mulch. If the herbicide was applied over the entire field, applying the plastic may destroy the weed barrier in the soil along the edges of the plastic strips. Weed management in the row middles is discussed in the next section.

Some herbicides may volatilize and cause crop injury when used under plastic mulches. One label (ethalfluralin) prohibits use under plastic mulches. Be careful to observe any precautions on the product label and, in the absence of experience, try the treatment on a small scale at first.

Weed Management between Plastic Mulch Strips

As is the case with bare-ground culture, weeds must be managed successfully between the crop rows in a plasticulture system (photo 8-1). Control methods may include herbicides, cultivation, flaming, hand weeding, or a combination of these. Timings for weed-management activities include stale bed, preemergence, and postemergence applications.

Much research has been conducted over the years concerning the influence of weeds in the row middles on crop yield and quality. The question most often asked is whether the combination of plastic mulch, under-plastic fertilizer, and drip irrigation can compensate for weed pressure in the row middles. In one series of studies, the influence of weeds in row middles was evaluated in pepper, tomato, and muskmelon (Bonanno and Lamont 1985, 1987; Bonanno 1986; Motsenbocker and Bonanno 1988, 1989). Overhead irrigation and drip irrigation were also compared in pepper, muskmelon, and tomato grown on plastic mulch (Bonanno 1987, 1988, 1989). On average, weeds in the row middles reduced yields 25–30% in all three crops with overhead irrigation/plastic mulch, and 55–60% in tomato and muskmelon with drip irrigation/ plastic mulch, when compared to using the best herbicide treatment for each crop. One explanation for this difference might be that when overhead irrigation is used, the roots of the weeds are evenly spread over the field (both under and between the plastic) (figure 8-1). When drip irrigation is used, especially in a dry year, competition is increased because both the crop roots and the weed roots are concentrated near the drip tube (figure 8-2).

Photo 8-1. Excellent control of weeds between the rows of plasticulture peppers.

Figure 8-1. With overhead irrigation, crop and weed roots are evenly distributed.

Source: George W. Hamilton, University of New Hampshire Cooperative Extension.

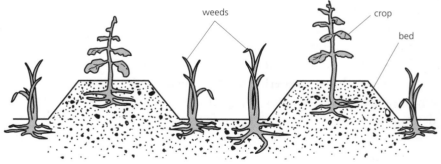

Figure 8-2. With drip irrigation, most crop and weed roots are near the drip tube.

Source: George W. Hamilton, University of New Hampshire Cooperative Extension.

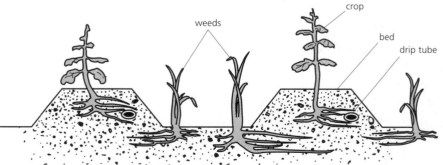

In another study conducted with tomato over three years, weeds in the row middles reduced yields by 75% (Abdul-Baki et al. 1997). In this study, no supplemental irrigation was applied, since adequate soil moisture was present during each growing season. In yet another study conducted with peppers grown in plasticulture, the critical period for weed control was found to be weeks four through ten (Ashley 1997). Significant yield losses occurred when weeds were allowed to grow during these weeks.

Stale-Bed Applications

Herbicide options are limited for many vegetable crops. When an herbicide is used in a crop, weed species may be present that the herbicide cannot control. Paraquat, glyphosate, pelargonic acid, or flaming with propane may be used to obtain early-season control of emerged weeds. When using flaming between the mulch, be careful not to melt the plastic. Because of this potential for melting, it is difficult to obtain effective control of weeds along the edges of the plastic with flaming. Hand weeding is often required as a supplement to the flaming, which may negate the effectiveness of the stale bed.

The principle of this technique is that most of the weed seeds near the soil surface will germinate within two weeks after soil preparation. Adequate soil moisture and temperature (at least 50°F at a depth of 2 inches) must be present for germination to occur. Application of one of the three herbicides mentioned above or flaming will kill these weeds. Provided that the soil is not further disturbed, seeds will not be moved to the soil surface where they can germinate.

Remember that these herbicides will not provide any residual weed control. Check current labels to determine registered uses by crop. For cucumber, melon, squash, pumpkin, pepper, and eggplant, glyphosate must be applied at least three days PRIOR to seeding or transplanting. Glyphosate can also be used for control or suppression of emerged perennial weeds.

Finally, any cultivations should be shallow (0.75–1 inch maximum) so as not to reposition any additional weed seeds at the soil surface. The stale-bed technique also will help to improve the performance of any residual herbicides applied, since a reduced number of viable weed seeds will be near the soil surface.

The steps involved in the stale-bed technique are outlined below:

1. Prepare the field and lay the plastic mulch as far ahead of seeding or transplanting as possible. In some areas, the plastic may be applied several months prior to transplanting (such as the previous fall). If a soil-incorporated herbicide will be used on the entire field, it must be applied and incorporated at this time. The soil should have adequate moisture (irrigate with at least 0.25 inch of water if necessary).

2. Wait as long as possible so that weeds will germinate and emerge between the plastic. Weed seedlings, especially grasses, should be allowed to grow to the third leaf stage. The first true leaf is a minimum stage of growth.

3. If transplants are being used, make an application of paraquat, pelargonic acid, or glyphosate (see labels) as a banded spray to the row middles, or flame the middles before transplanting the crop into the mulch.

4. If the crop will be seeded, the herbicide or flaming may be applied just before or just after seeding as long as the crop has not yet emerged (see labels).

Special Precautions

Some special precautions are in order with glyphosate. If glyphosate is used as a broadcast application or if excessive glyphosate comes in contact with the plastic mulch, overhead irrigation or rainfall is required before planting to wash the excess glyphosate off the plastic. Glyphosate does not photodegrade to any great extent while on the surface of the plastic (Gilreath 1987). It is also very water-soluble. There have been numerous instances in which glyphosate from the mulch surface was dissolved by the transplant water from a water-wheel-type transplanter and carried into the plant hole just before the transplants were set (Bonanno 1999). Glyphosate is inactivated by clay, but since most transplants are produced in soilless mixes containing no clay, the roots of the transplants can absorb the glyphosate just prior to the closing of the transplant hole. This scenario has resulted in crop injury or crop death. Injury appears as blotchy chlorosis followed by necrosis and/or viruslike symptoms. This situation is also possible with paraquat, although paraquat does photodegrade on the plastic surface. Transplanting should be delayed at least 96 hours (four days) after the application of paraquat to mitigate the injury potential (Gilreath 1986). The best way to avoid this situation altogether is to apply the herbicide carefully to the row middles and avoid a broadcast application to the plastic. Data is not yet available on pelargonic acid.

Flaming with propane can be used instead of paraquat, pelargonic acid, or glyphosate. Flaming will kill many emerged annual broadleaf weeds. However, success with small annual grasses is limited, as the growing point may not yet be emerged. As noted above, excess heat along the edge of the row middle will melt the plastic, so some hand weeding is usually necessary to control weeds near the plastic edges.

Delayed Stale-Bed Technique

In many cases, labels exist for the use of paraquat or pelargonic acid after transplanting or after the seeded crop has emerged. This is considered a delayed stale-bed application. The advantages of delaying the application of paraquat, pelargonic acid, or flaming until after transplanting or crop emergence is that a longer period exists for weed emergence. Many growers apply plastic mulch too close to transplanting, so there is not enough time for weeds to emerge prior to planting. Delayed applications require shielding to eliminate possible crop contact by the spray.

When building or using a shield, follow a few guidelines. Shield the spray, not the crop. A full shield (top, front, back, and sides) is preferred over traditional shields that protect only on the sides. The shield should be slightly wider than the row middle so that no skips are made along the plastic. The shield should be used slightly above the plastic to avoid tearing the plastic, so an apron should hang below the shield on all sides as a flexible buffer for the spray. Plastic film or some other nonabsorbent material can be used for the apron. Avoid burlap or other fabrics, as they will absorb the chemical and act as a wick applicator, causing crop injury. Even with a shield, windy conditions should be avoided. Even the best shields will allow some move-ment of herbicide past the shield, and this movement will be accentuated under windy conditions.

Residual Applications

Residual herbicides are often recommended for weed control between rows of plastic mulch. Depending on the crop, preplant-incorporated and/or preemergence herbicides may be labeled for such use. Both types of applications require some precautions.

If a preplant-incorporated herbicide is used, it must be applied and incorporated prior to applying the plastic mulch, since incorporating an herbicide into the row middles is very difficult if beds are used. Proper incorporation is much easier if raised beds are not used. Unless they have specialized equipment that can incorporate herbicide to the proper depth while not significantly destroying the beds, many growers avoid preplant-incorporated herbicides. Some herbicides, such as clomazone or bensulide, must be very shallowly incorporated to avoid crop injury and be effective. Care must also be taken to maintain an herbicide layer next to the plastic strips. As mentioned earlier, two of the most successful types of incorporation tools on beds are narrow rototiller units and rolling cultivators run in tandem over the beds.

Use only a labeled preemergence herbicide between the plastic strips, before or after planting. In addition to being illegal, use of nonlabeled herbicides may result in crop injury or death either from the herbicide moving with water under the plastic or from the crop roots growing past the edges of the plastic. Also, do not broadcast residual herbicides over the plastic. The excess herbicide around the plant holes can wash into the holes with rain or irrigation, greatly concentrating the herbicide and potentially causing crop stunting, injury, or death. Application booms must be set up to band the herbicide between the plastic. Growers often spray onto the edge of the plastic to avoid untreated soil areas along the edges of the plastic (figures 8-3 and 8-4, page 80).

When banded applications of herbicides are used, remember to calculate the actual area of soil that is being sprayed per acre of crop (with 30-inch beds and 30-inch middles, for example, only half the total amount of herbicide would be required per acre since only half the amount of soil area per acre is being sprayed). Fol-

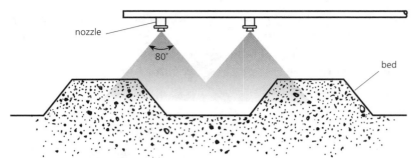

Figure 8-3. 80° even flat-fan nozzles (two nozzles).

Source: George W. Hamilton, University of New Hampshire Cooperative Extension.

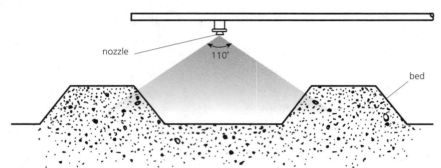

Figure 8-4. 110° even flat-fan nozzle.

Source: George W. Hamilton, University of New Hampshire Cooperative Extension.

low label directions for banded applications.

In some cases, combinations of herbicides and application timings may be used to increase the weed-control spectrum. In tomato, for example, trifluralin may be incorporated over the entire field prior to applying the plastic mulch, and metribuzin may be applied to the row middles after transplanting. Note that herbicide labels generally do not mention the use of plastic mulches unless the use is not allowed or precautions are necessary. Unless the label specifies otherwise, herbicides can be used in combination with plasticulture as long as all label directions are followed, including the herbicide rate and placement, timing, and crop planted.

A potential problem for small growers is the diversity of crops that may be grown in a small area with different crops in adjacent rows. In this case, the stale-bed technique may be more appropriate. Residual herbicides may be limited because of variations in crop tolerance and label restrictions. Growers should try to group crops based on herbicide registrations. For example, in most of the United States, napropamide could be used in an area where pepper, tomato, egg-plant, cabbage, cauliflower, and broccoli will be grown in adjacent rows. However, use of metribuzin for additional broadleaf weed control in tomato might not be possible if the tomatoes are growing next to a crop where metribuzin is not registered. If several rows of tomatoes are grown, the metribuzin could be used in all rows except the side of the tomato row that is next to another crop. It is unclear what the required width of an untreated buffer strip should be; however, a width equivalent to the crop row spacing is a minimum distance.

Postemergence Applications

Postemergence possibilities exist for several vegetable crops. These may include selective herbicides such as metribuzin or sethoxydim, nonselective herbicides including paraquat and pelargonic acid, and flaming. As of this writing, glyphosate is not registered for any postemergence applications in vegetable crops after the crop is emerged. One disadvantage of many postemergence herbicides is that they have no residual activity, thus requiring repeated applications. It is advisable to use a residual herbicide in most cases and to supplement it with a postemergence application if it is both labeled and needed.

For selective postemergence herbicide use, follow the same precautions mentioned for surface-applied preemergence herbicides in the previous section. These include banding the herbicide between the plastic and minimizing herbicide contact with the plastic to avoid runoff into the planting holes. Additionally, label precautions required for the use of any postemergence herbicide in bare-ground culture must be followed in plasticulture.

In some cases, paraquat is registered for use between plastic mulch while the crop is present. These uses are much more limited than the broad stale-bed registrations described previously; however, many state registrations exist beyond those that are on the national label. Pelargonic acid was registered for use in many crops in 1997. Both of these herbicides are nonselective and provide contact burnback of green tissue. Special care must be taken with these herbicides to avoid crop injury. In all cases, paraquat and pelargonic acid must be applied with a shielded sprayer to the row middle. Contact with the crop may cause necrosis of that crop part within 24 hours. For example, if one vine from a cucumber plant is sprayed, only that vine will die; there will be no translocation back to the rest of the plant. Glyphosate should not be used between the plastic during the season. Glyphosate is a nonselective and translocated herbicide. Contact with only the tip of the cucumber vine described above may result in death of the entire plant. Glyphosate should only be used as a stale-bed treatment or after the crop is harvested for control of emerged perennial weeds. As shielding technology changes, the restrictions on glyphosate may change. Labels may change, so be sure to read them and their recommendations to be advised of potential use and rate changes.

Backpack sprayers or hand-held boom sprayers are often used for herbicide applications in plasticulture systems. Be sure to calibrate them properly and maintain a constant pressure by monitoring with a pressure gauge, especially on hand-pumped models. Use caution when spraying paraquat or pelargonic acid with a backpack or hand-held sprayer; follow all of the precautions and restrictions on the label. Spray when the wind is calm to avoid spray drift to crop plants. Even with calm conditions, using a shield is the best way to minimize crop contact. For both paraquat and pelargonic acid, always use a surfactant and sufficient water to obtain good control.

Flaming between plastic can be tricky. This is primarily because it is likely that the plastic will melt, lose its contact with the soil, and blow away. Growers usually suggest using a shield or orienting the burners away from the edges of the plastic. Flaming between plastic can be easier with clear plastic than with black, because the condensation under clear plastic reduces the potential for melting (Grubinger and Else 1995). Practically speaking, it is difficult to get close enough to the plastic edge to avoid the need for mechanical removal of weeds along the mulch edge.

Cultivation

Cultivation is used by some growers for weed control in the row middles (Bowman 1997). Some factors need to be considered. Cultivation equipment should be narrow, and high-clearance tractors should be used. Growers without these tools often leave wide row middles to allow a tractor to pass between the rows of plastic. This results in row middles of 6–10 feet or more compared to row middles of 2–3 feet, which are common when herbicides or specialized cultivation tools are used.

Cultivation equipment should be designed to cultivate to the edge of the plastic while not tearing it. Some growers have designed equipment to lift the mulch slightly, cultivate shallowly just under it, and add soil back to cover the edge of the plastic (Grubinger and Else 1995).

In all cases, weeds should be cultivated when they are very small. When weeds are small, they can be buried by the action of the cultivator and be cut or uprooted. Finally, never cultivate more rows at once than were applied by a single pass of a plastic mulching machine. "Guess middles" (row middles created between passes of equipment) are rarely consistent in width, and excessive tearing of the plastic or uncultivated areas can result.

Cover Crops

As an alternative to cultivation and residual herbicides, some growers have tried planting a cover crop in the row middles. The premise is that the cover crop will outcompete the weeds. However, if the cover is more competitive than the weeds, it will reduce yields at least as much as the weeds.

There are at least two ways to avert competition. One is to apply the plastic mulch and plant the cover crop long enough before planting to establish a thick cover in the row middles. Before planting, desiccate the cover crop with glyphosate, pelargonic acid, or paraquat and rely on the dead cover to suppress the weeds. The second method is to plant the cover crop at the same time the crop is planted and rely on mowing to suppress the cover. This will not eliminate the competition but will reduce it. Several growers have reported that mowing is time-consuming and hard on equipment. It may still be an option for some, but many growers who have tried mowing have abandoned the technique. In one study, a living legume cover crop reduced yields of peppers by 60% (Else 1995). This study was done with equal plastic and row middle widths as well as slightly raised beds (2–4 inches).

Although very little research has been done in this area, it is likely that plastic width, bed height, frequency of mowing, and choice of cover crop may influence cover crop competition. Advantages of cover crops include improved trafficability and reduced soil erosion. Note that cover crop selection varies with location; consult local experts to determine which cover crops will grow best in your area. Winter hardiness may also be a factor in cover crop selection.

Weed Management under Row Covers

Row covers of single and multiple row widths are sometimes used by growers just after planting a crop during cool weather conditions. They help warm the soil and air around the crop. From a weed-management standpoint, this warmer environment contributes to early germination of weed seeds and rapid growth of weeds once they emerge. It is not uncommon to see lush weed growth under a row cover and no weed growth between the covers. Row covers can create serious problems for growers who rely on cultivation for weed control. By the time the cover is removed, the weeds may be so large that hand-weeding may be the only option available.

When using herbicides for weed management under row covers, several points need to be considered. From an application and activation standpoint, the same information described above for use of herbicides under plastic mulch applies. Most importantly, if a solid plastic row cover is used, activation of a preemergence herbicide may be poor, resulting in excessive weed growth. With fabric row covers, rainfall and irrigation water can move freely through the cover, so surface-applied herbicides could be activated after the cover is applied. The only advantage here is that the field can be prepared, the crop seeded or transplanted, the herbicide applied, and the row cover applied all in rapid succession. Once the row cover is applied, the field can be irrigated. Another difference to consider is that weed emergence will be slow between the row covers, in many cases affording some additional time before treatment is required in the row middles. It is important to pay close attention to weed emergence patterns to avoid poor weed control caused by an herbicide application or activation that is too late.

Herbicide use under row covers can result in crop injury. Although several herbicides can be used safely under row covers, some uses can cause or contribute to crop injury and even crop death. Generally, ventilated (perforated, slit, or fabric) covers are safer than solid covers or hotcaps from an herbicide-injury standpoint. This is especially true with an herbicide that is moderately or highly volatile. Prior testing on a small scale is strongly recommended before making these applications on a large scale. In one case, use of ethalfluralin is prohibited by the label under mulches and row covers due to the potential for crop injury.

Remember that improper use of some row covers can, in itself, cause crop injury. For example, many cultivars of sweet corn, especially supersweets and sugar-enhanced ones, do not germinate well in cold soils. When a grower plants corn in cold soils and then places a row cover over the rows, poor germination and emergence can still result. In many cases, the soil does not warm fast enough, and the corn seed imbibes cold water, which will slow germination. While herbicide use do not cause the problem, it can accentuate it (Bonanno 1991). If the soil temperature is adequate and row covers are ventilated, the likelihood of crop injury is greatly reduced.

Another example involves high temperatures. Although solid clear tunnels are excellent for rapid soil-warming, excessive air temperatures under the cover can kill the crop. This can result regardless of whether or not an herbicide was used. It is important to monitor air temperatures under row covers and ventilate or remove covers if the air temperature becomes extreme. It is not uncommon for air temperatures under row covers to reach over 120°F.

Summary

In conclusion, weed management in plasticulture requires a higher level of attention than in bare-ground culture. Be certain to obtain state or local university recommendations to verify which products are registered for use in your area. Observing all of the guidelines above will go a long way toward ensuring effective weed control with minimal adverse crop effects.

CHAPTER 9

Soil Sanitation—Managing Soilborne Pests

Steve Olson

Many soilborne pests can cause economic damage to a crop. These include bacteria, fungi, insects, nematodes, and weeds. At times, it may be necessary to suppress or control these pests before the crop is planted to improve plant quality and vigor, increase yields, and thus increase potential profitability. The many approaches to suppressing soil pests include both nonchemical and chemical methods or combinations of the two.

Nonchemical Methods

Biological Control

To date, no biocontrol agents have been used successfully to control nematodes. However, biological control agents have been used to suppress certain soilborne pathogens such as *Pythium, Phytophthora,* and *Rhizoctonia solani.*

There are several shortcomings of using biocontrol for soilborne plant pathogens. Some of the introduced biocontrol agents are specific to only one of several diseases that may be important to a crop. Many biocontrol agents may provide only partial control of the pathogen or fail to survive long enough to be of benefit.

Biocontrol for soil insects has been tried using predacious nematodes, but results have been mixed. Biocontrol for weeds has been investigated, but at this time there are no commercial biocontrol agents for vegetables that have proven to be an effective method of weed control.

Crop Rotation

For crop rotation to be effective, crops unsuitable for the target pest must be selected and introduced into a rotation cycle. The length of rotation depends upon the persistence of the pest. Rotation may be as short as two to three years for black rot of the crucifer crops to as long as four or more years for *Fusarium* wilt of watermelons. For some problems, such as bacterial wilt of tomatoes, even long-term rotation may not be effective as a management tool. For weed management, alternative crops may be selected for which there are herbicides available, the weed problem can then be managed in the alternative crop but not in the traditional crop.

Cover crops can be used during off-season production to reduce or suppress a pest. For a cover crop to be effective, stands must be established quickly and undesirable weeds, which can serve as an alternative host, must be controlled. Given that many different weeds can serve as alternative hosts to nematodes, it may not be possible to manage nematodes with cover crops unless weeds are managed. However, research in Washington State has demonstrated that planting pure stands of certain sorghum-sudan hybrids (such as Trudan 8) can reduce nematode populations.

Crop rotation may be limited as a strategy because of limited land, expense of cover crops, ability to market an alternative crop, or specialized equipment needed to produce an alternative crop.

Fallowing

Fallowing during the off-season can be a very effective control method for soil pests. When weed or crop growth is prevented, food sources are no longer available for the soil pest. Weeds are destroyed as they germinate and not allowed to set seed. A minimum of at least two discing operations may be required to maintain clean fallow conditions during the off-season. More discing may be necessary if regrowth occurs. Using an herbicide to keep the field clean is not as effective, especially with nematodes. Bringing them to the surface and exposing them to the drying action of the sun can further reduce populations.

Fallowing has several disadvantages, such as increasing oxidation of organic matter, increasing hardpan area with extensive cultivation, and increasing soil erosion through wind and water action.

Flooding

Flooding can be accomplished only when certain soil conditions occur. The water level must be controllable so that the land can be covered in water. This can occur when an impermeable layer of soil occurs or high water tables are present. This technique has shown to be effective against certain soil pests, especially nematodes. Alternating two- to three-week cycles between flooding and drying is more effective than long, continuous flooding. One problem with the alternating cycles is that soil nutrients such as nitrogen can also be flushed when the water is removed.

Plant Resistance

For some pests, genetic resistance can be a very valuable tool for growers. For some diseases such as *Verticillium* and *Fusarium* wilt of tomatoes, excellent resistance is available. But for bacterial wilt of tomatoes, poor to no resistance is available. In most seed catalogs, the resistance for each variety is listed.

For nematodes, very few crops have resistance. In tomato, a single dominant gene imparts resistance to root-knot nematodes. This has been used for many years in home garden and processing varieties. Lately, a few commercial varieties have been released with the resistant gene. It is not appropriate to rely only on genetic resistance, since resistance-breaking root-knot strains have been found, and resistance is not complete at higher soil temperatures. In pepper, two new varieties have been released ('Carolina Belle' and 'Carolina Wonder') from the U.S. Department of Agriculture with resistance to root-knot nematodes. These varieties have shown high levels of resistance, but yields are below that of other commercial varieties. With most other crops (except southern peas), nematode resistance is lacking, especially with vine crops.

One problem with genetic resistance is that it is usually specific for only one race of a disease, such a *Fusarium* wilt of tomato. At this time, most tomato varieties released have resistance to both race 1 and 2, but a new race (race 3) has shown up, and only a few tomato cultivars have resistance incorporated for all three races of *Fusarium*. Another example is bacterial leaf spot resistance in pepper to races 1, 2, and 3. This can be a constant problem with genetic resistance, since the soil pathogens can constantly evolve and overcome the resistance that breeders incorporate.

Soil Amendments

Many different types of amendments have been applied to soils to suppress populations of soil pests and improve plant health and crop yields. These materials include animal wastes, composted materials, seaweed meals, and cover crop residues incorporated by discing. An added benefit of these materials is improved soil fertility, organic matter content, water-holding capacity, nutrient retention, and cation exchange capacity.

Suppressing soilborne pests by using amendments is reputedly based on enhanced microbial activity and increased number of antagonists generated by the decomposition of the amendment in the soil. Soils with a diversity of beneficial microorganisms are more suppressive to pathogens than soils with little or no biological diversity. Other possible mechanisms for pathogen suppression by amendments include direct inhibition of the pathogen or reduced infectivity of the organisms into the plant host. Population increases of beneficial organisms in soil appears to be the direct result of environmental changes brought about by the amendments after they are added to the soil, suggesting that to sustain soil suppressiveness, amendments must be reapplied periodically to the soil. Much of the past and current research seems to indicate that the major effects of soil amendments to crop yields appear to be less related to soil pest control than to enhanced plant nutrition and nutrient and water availability.

Soil Solarization

Soil solarization is a nonchemical method in which moist raised beds are covered with a clear polyethylene film for strip solarization (photos 9-1 and 9-2), or an area is fully tarped for a six- to 12-week period for full-field solarization (photo 9-3) to elevate soil temperatures to a level that is lethal to soil pests. Soil temperatures are elevated because incoming solar radiation is trapped under the clear film, reducing the dissipation of heat from the soil. To be effective, soils must be wet when the film is applied, and moisture must be maintained during the solarization period to increase the susceptibility of the soilborne pests and increase the heat movement through the soil. At the end of the solarization period before the crop is planted, the film must be painted either white to cool the soil for a late-summer crop or black to exclude light for a late fall/winter crop (photo 9-4). A poor

paint job can result in elevated temperatures and poor growth or problems with weed growth under the mulch when soil temperatures cool down.

Soil solarization appears to be most successful in heavier rather than sandy soils due to the better water-holding capacity of heavy soils, which can increase heat transfer to deeper areas. The degree of pest control is directly related to the depth to which lethal temperatures are reached. The depth to which lethal temperatures can be achieved is dependent on the intensity and duration of sunlight and ambient temperature. Because of these conditions, soil solarization is only possible during the hot summer months.

No benefit has been seen from solarizing one year and waiting until the next year to plant; thus, it should only be used for fall crops or overwintering crops such as strawberries. If drip tapes are used under the clear film, they must be buried to prevent pinholes that form

Photo 9-1. Strip application of clear mulch for solarization.

Photo 9-3. Full-field application of clear mulch for solarization.

Photo 9-2. Soil solarization using clear polyethylene mulch.

Photo 9-4. Spraying clear mulch white before fall planting of tomatoes.

as a result of the sun's rays being magnified through water beads that form under the film.

Solarization has been shown to suppress several soil pests such as reniform nematode *(Rotylenchulus reniformis)*, stubby root nematode *(Paratrichodorus minor)*, ring nematode *(Criconemella* species), and southern stem blight *(Sclerotium rolfsii).* However, the suppression has not always been consistent. Solarization has been most consistent in the control of the perennial nutsedges (photo 9-5). It has not been shown to control root-knot nematodes; a combination of methods may be needed to control this pest. In Florida, solarization has been tried on several crops (tomatoes, peppers, and strawberries) with good results.

Other Cultural Practices

Other cultural practices that can be used to reduce soilborne pest problems include the following:

1. Rapid destruction of the present crop after harvest. Fields that are disced as soon as possible after harvest is completed will not only prevent further pest buildup but subject existing populations to dissipation by sun and wind.

2. Use of pest-free transplants. Many pest problems can be brought to the field through infected transplants. Also, by using transplants, the crop is not subjected to pests in the soil for as long a period, especially during the early but critical period of development.

3. Use of clean irrigation and spray water. While this may not be a main source of problems, it is possible to spread disease and nematodes through dirty water.

Photo 9-5. Effect of solarization on yellow nutsedge control; left bed untreated, right bed solarized.

Chemical Control

Nonfumigants

Nonfumigant materials work by directly killing the target organism or by preventing its entrance into the root system. Most of the materials are very target-specific, and many times control is dependent upon how well the material is incorporated and distributed throughout the soil. Most of the nonfumigants have some residual activity. Nonfumigant materials are available as fungicides, nematicides, insecticides, and herbicides. Insecticides and herbicides will not be discussed, as they are covered elsewhere in this guide.

Fungicides. Several fungicides are labeled for use under mulches. They can be contact materials or systemic materials. Some systemic materials can be applied through the drip lines or applied to the foliage. Most of these materials are very specific and may target only a single organism. Examples are mefenoxam and PCNB.

Nematicides. All of the currently registered nonfumigant nematicides are labeled for soil application. Examples are ethoprop, fenamiphos, and oxamyl. Oxamyl is also labeled for foliar application to suppress nematode damage.

Nematicides must be uniformly applied to the area where the root system is to be protected. They must be incorporated into the soil or carried into the soil by water. Failure to uniformly incorporate the materials will result in poor control, since the material must come in contact with nematodes to kill them. Placement within the top 2–4 inches of soil should provide a zone of protection for seed germination or transplant establishment and protect early-season root growth. Nematode management must be thought of as a preplant consideration, because once root infection occurs and plant damage becomes visible, it is generally too late to avoid significant yield losses.

Performance of the nonfumigant nematicides has been inconsistent in controlling pests and in obtaining economic returns to the grower, especially when they are compared to methyl bromide or other broad-spectrum fumigants. Many of the materials are reasonably mobile and are readily leached in a sandy, low-organic-matter soil, so special consideration must be given to irrigation practices and management. Some are used by soil microorganisms as a food source, and rapid decomposition can occur. The success of rescue attempts through foliar application of oxamyl depends upon how early the damage is found. Many of the nonfumigant nematicides also have some degree of soil-insect control. Check labels to see which crops are cleared.

Fumigants

Soil fumigants will only control those pests that are present in the treated area. All of them have some ability to fume or move from the point of application. This ability to move is what can make fumigants so effective. After treatment, growers must be careful not to reintroduce pest problems through contaminated soil, water, equipment, personnel, or plant material. The various fumigants differ in their effectiveness, but one thing they all have in common is the requirement for a good soil-surface seal after application. This is to prevent premature loss of the fumigant or to maintain a high concentration for a long enough time to be effective.

1,3-D (1,3-Dichloropropene). 1,3-D is currently used as a preplant fumigant only. It is only effective against nematodes and certain arthropods, specifically wireworms and symphylans. 1,3-D comes as a liquid that, when injected into the soil, volatilizes into a gas and penetrates through the soil mass. It is usually applied using a pressurized system but may also be applied with a gravity-flow rig. The most common application method is with chisels spaced 12 inches apart and 12 or more inches deep. To prevent premature loss of the fumigant, it is extremely important to destroy the chisel traces through bedding over, pressing a bed and applying a mulch, discing or cultivating the field, or using offset chisels. Soil temperatures at the depth of application should be 40°–80°F. Application may be in-row, in-bed, or broadcast. Soil moisture should be adequate (50% field capacity). Soil that is too dry allows rapid escape of the fumigant, and soil that is too wet will not allow diffusion of the product, resulting in poor activity. Heavy rains after application may reduce effectiveness and increase time to planting. Normally, at least three weeks are needed

from application to planting. In some areas, fall fumigation has worked well. Some formulations of 1,3-D come with chloropicrin added (17% or 35%) to increase its effectiveness against soilborne pathogens. Also, some new formulations are available as emulsifiable concentrates and may be applied through drip lines. 1,3-D is cleared for most vegetable crops, but check the label before use.

Chloropicrin. Chloropicrin is used infrequently as a stand-alone fumigant. It is usually mixed with methyl bromide or 1,3-D. It is a highly effective material against soilborne pathogens but is inconsistent for nematode control and shows little to no activity against weeds. Application is by a pressurized system with chisels spaced 12 inches apart and 8–12 inches deep. Immediately after application, the fumigated area must be sealed or tarped to retard escape of the fumigant (photos 9-6 and 9-7). Soil temperatures should be from 40°–80° F, and soil moisture should be adequate (about 50% field capacity). Chloropicrin material is highly toxic to animals, including humans.

Dazomet. Dazomet is a general soil biocide. At this time, it not approved for use on food crops but may be used in tobacco, ornamentals (including cut flowers), and turf seedbeds. Dazomet comes as a granule with 98% active ingredient. When the granule comes in contact with moisture in the soil, it is broken down into methyl isothiocyanate (MITC). It is active on some weeds, insects, nematodes and soilborne fungi. Dazomet is applied to the soil surface and incorporated to the depth to which control is desired. After application, the soil surface needs to be sealed by water, compaction, or polyethylene film. Thorough incorporation is necessary since MITC diffuses very little. Soil moisture needs to be from 50% to 80% of field capacity to get rapid release of the MITC. If soil moisture is not adequate, then all of the material may not break down until additional moisture is present, which will result in erratic control or crop injury. The optimum soil temperature for application is from 50° to 80°F.

Metham-Sodium. Metham-sodium can be a good preplant fumigant, provided it comes in contact with

Photo 9-6. Bed fumigation and mulch application.

Photo 9-7. Bed fumigation and mulch application (different view).

the target organism. It is considered to be a general soil biocide. When diluted with water or in contact with soil, it breaks down to its active ingredient, MITC. It can be somewhat inconsistent in controlling nematodes and some weeds, especially nutsedge. It is fairly effective against soil fungi. Application methods include chiseling in, drip application, spray blades, injection wheels, application through overhead irrigation systems, and surface application followed by rotovating or watering in. When using chisels, the distance apart should be no farther than 5 inches due to the limited movement of MITC. Because of its solubility in water, it lends itself to drip application and especially for double-cropping, where it can be used to kill the first crop and a subsequent application made for pest control. When chisel-applied or rotovated in, the moisture level needs to be high (near field capac-

ity) for the metham-sodium to work properly. Soil may need to be sealed depending upon the application method. This can be accomplished by water application, rolling, or laying a polyethylene mulch. Metham-sodium is moderately toxic to humans and other animals. See the label for specific uses. The 42% active ingredient material weighs 10 pounds per gallon. Metham-sodium is labeled for all crops.

Methyl Bromide. Methyl bromide (Mbr) is a highly effective preplant-applied biocide, but because of its implications in affecting the ozone layer, it is scheduled for total phaseout by January 1, 2005. The phaseout is taking place in increments, and the last reduction took place on January 1, 2003. The resulting effect on cost and availability has made Mbr uneconomical for vegetable production. Its broad range of control includes nematodes, soil insects, some soilborne diseases, and many weeds. It can be very effective against perennial sedges when proper rates are used. It comes as liquefied gas stored under pressure in containers that vary in weight from 1.5 pounds to over 1,000 pounds (pigs) (photo 9-8, page 90). It has the greatest volatility of any of the fumigants, and diffusion in soil can be up to 36 inches. Because it is heavier than air, it has a tendency to sink or settle in low places. MBr is applied with a pressurized system with chisels spaced 12 inches apart and 8–12 inches deep (photo 9-9, page 90). Immediately after application, the fumigated area needs to be tarped unless the material is deeply placed (18 inches or more), injection shank traces are destroyed, and the soil surface is compacted. Application may be made in-row (for deep place-

---

SAFETY PRECAUTIONS WHEN USING FUMIGANTS

All fumigants are hazardous to humans. It is important to read the label and make sure that the proper safety equipment is used or available when applying these materials. They all pose potential inhalation and dermal exposure health risks. For some of the products, special training is required for the applicators. Fumigation should never be done by an individual alone in the field.

Photo 9-8. Fumigation tanks mounted on front of tractor.

Photo 9-9. Soil fumigation being done at the time of application of black plastic mulch and drip irrigation.

ment), in-bed, or broadcast. For spot treatment, small cans can be used and injections made under a tarp into an evaporation pan. The optimum soil temperature at injection depth is 50°–85°F. Soil moisture levels may range from 30% to 70% of field capacity, but if deep injection is used, soil moisture below 50% field capacity is preferred. The time from application to planting can vary from one to three weeks, depending upon environmental conditions.

All Mbr formulations used in field production have a percentage of chloropicrin in them. At low concentrations (2%), the chloropicrin is used as a warning agent, since Mbr is colorless and odorless. At higher concentrations, the chloropicrin increases the effectiveness of the mixture against soilborne pathogens. Since labeled crops can vary by state, labels must be consulted before use.

Production of Strawberries Using Plasticulture

Joseph A. Fiola

Strawberry production has been a significant part of the diverse agriculture in the Northeast for U-pick, roadside, and wholesale fresh markets, and for processing. Many locations in the region have the climate and soils needed to produce quality berries; however, in recent years acreage devoted to matted-row strawberry production has decreased. Reasons for the decrease in acreage include decreased profitability due to high dependence on hand labor; competition from western producers; and limited productivity, quality, and fruit shelf-life of existing varieties.

The annual plasticulture strawberry system used in California and the southeastern United States has increased yield and fruit quality significantly over conventional matted-row plantings and is rapidly being adopted for use in the Northeast (photo 10-1). The high-density system maximizes the reproductive efficiency of the strawberry plant, requiring only nine months from planting to harvest, as compared to the 14 months required by the matted-row system. Late-summer planting directs vegetative energy into branch crowns instead of runners and also avoids the heat,

Photo 10-1. Annual plasticulture strawberry system.

drought, weed, and disease pressures of midsummer. The short growth period (plant in August/September, harvest in mid-May) allows efficient land use for double-cropping and ease of rotation.

Establishment costs are higher for plasticulture than matted-row production; however, production is of higher quality and is earlier, when crop value is highest. Labor costs are typically reduced, as there is no need for blossom removal, setting of daughter plants, or hand-weeding, and fruit is more easily and efficiently harvested from the beds. The limitation and/or risks of the system include high establishment costs (costs for plastic mulch, plants, drip irrigation, and floating row covers); a limited growth period for flower bud initiation in the fall; and winter injury causing reduced growth and fruiting. Research is being conducted to make strawberry plasticulture practical in the Northeast, and dedicated growers have found high profitability utilizing the system.

The Basics of the System

There are many critical parameters of the system, all of which are important to optimal production and efficiency. Since this is an integrated system, all of the components are important, and any "weak link" or cutting of a component can lead to failure. The late-summer-planted system includes raised beds, black plastic mulch, drip irrigation, high-density planting, and floating row covers.

Climate Considerations

The references in this chapter to "warmer climates" will refer to the areas in the eastern United States that Darrow (1966) identified as zones for late-winter strawberry flower initiation. These include the east-

■ 91 ■

ern coastal plain of North and South Carolina, the central Piedmont region of North Carolina, and farther south into Piedmont South Carolina and Georgia, where yields can range from 1 to 2 pounds per plant in good seasons.

The bulk of this chapter will deal with managing the system in more northern locations. Over the past ten years, research in New Jersey, Maryland, and Virginia (referred to as the mid-Atlantic) has helped to move the system northward. Growers in the northern Piedmont region of Virginia, the Eastern Shore of Maryland, and southwestern New Jersey are consistently achieving yields of 1 pound per plant, but additional management costs and risks are involved. This success has initiated successful expansion far into the Northeast region, again with additional management strategies and risks. A thorough understanding of the principles and practices of the system is critical for success in these "more limiting" locations.

This system has given highest yields at locations with long growing seasons, typically 190 frost-free days with 3,200 growing degree hours. A limitation of the system is the risk of low yields due to a restricted time frame for plant growth and flower bud initiation in the fall in some locations and/or seasons. Floating row covers become even more critical as sites become more "marginal" (see discussion below). Select fields that are protected from northwesterly winds to minimize wind desiccation. A southern exposure will hinder plant growth and development in the fall, winter, and spring.

Preplant Preparation

Soil Considerations

Strawberries perform best on soils with high organic matter that have never been planted to strawberries or on land that has been in a proper crop rotation. These considerations are best for both reducing soil pests and maintaining soil organic matter. Light- to medium-textured soils with medium to high organic matter are best for bed preparation, nutrition management, and plant development in strawberry plasticulture. When the soil organic matter levels are too low (less than 1%), a season of cover-cropping is recommended before planting. Typically, beds are not made until August for a September planting, which allows for adequate cover crop growth in the same season prior to planting.

Management of Soil Pests

The plasticulture system incorporates integrated crop management practices that reduce the crop's vulnerability to pests. Plastic mulch–covered raised beds reduce diseases by improving soil drainage around the plant roots and protecting the fruit from splashing water. Also, the beds are typically maintained for only one to two seasons, in contrast to three to five seasons for matted rows, thereby reducing the time that pests have to get established. Many growers in the Northeast have been successful without fumigation, especially when planting onto virgin ground or land that has been dedicated to the proper rotation.

Fumigation with methyl bromide, chloropicrin, or both has been the standard practice in California, Florida, and North Carolina. Fumigation is recommended where weeds and soilborne diseases are a problem, especially where strawberries or solanaceous crops (such as tomatoes and peppers) were previously planted. Fumigation may help reduce the incidence and severity of red stele (*Phytophthora*) and *Verticillium* wilt; however, problems with *Pythium, Rhizoctonia,* and the black-root-rot complex may be exacerbated.

Fumigant can be applied to the whole field, shanked into the beds just before laying the plastic, or injected through the drip tape under the plastic, depending on the fumigant. For proper fumigant effectiveness, the soil should be well worked, free of plant debris, adequately moist, and warmer than 50°F. Fumigant should be applied at least two weeks prior to planting. It is always best to pop holes in the plastic the day before planting to allow any remaining fumigant to escape.

Nutrition

Sample the soil and have it tested to determine the pH and specific nutritional needs. Adjust soil pH to 6.0 with calcitic or dolomitic lime depending on the calcium (Ca) and magnesium (Mg) levels. Research in the mid-Atlantic region has shown that the plants need a total of 90–120 pounds of actual nitrogen (N) and 200–250 pounds of potassium (K) per acre per season. The high end (120 pounds N per acre) is recommended for sandy soils in warmer regions with mild winters and extended harvest seasons. In most locations in the mid-Atlantic and northern states, especially areas with heavier soils and earlier fall frost dates, 90 total pounds of N per acre is sufficient. The N application is typically split into a preplant incorporation and a harvest-season fertigation.

Broadcast and work into beds one-half of the needed N (60–70 pounds N per acre) as a 1-1-1 fertilizer [if the soil test shows low or medium levels of phosphorus (P) and K], and apply additional P and K according to the soil-test recommendations. Typically, 120 pounds of K per acre, preferably as potassium sulfate, is preplant-incorporated. Thirty pounds of P_2O_5 are added only when soil tests reveal very low phosphorus. If the soil test shows high or very high levels of P and K, use ammonium nitrate. Many bed makers can be modified to include a dry fertilizer injector that can incorporate the desired amount of granular fertilizer directly into the bed.

An additional 30–60 pounds of N per acre should be added through the drip system in the spring. In the Northeast, this can be a single application or two to three smaller applications on a seven- to ten-day schedule. North Carolina recommendations call for three applications two to three weeks apart, starting at the first signs of growth. Plants on lighter soils benefit from split applications. Recent research has shown that it is critical to have most of the N in the soil by early bloom for optimal set and yield and best to make the last application shortly after the first harvest. Additional N can be fertigated later, if necessary, during an extended harvest season.

The strawberry plasticulture system is also amenable to the use of organic sources of N. In experiments in New Jersey and Maryland, the yield using organic N nutrition treatments (Plant Tone, corn gluten meal, poultry manure) was comparable or superior to yields seen with conventional inorganic N plots. Since organic N is a slow-release form that resists leaching, all of the N can be preplant-incorporated, eliminating the increased cost, effort, and equipment necessary for spring fertigation.

Tissue Testing

Proper N nutrition is critical for optimal quantity and quality of production. Therefore, Florida and North Carolina have developed guidelines to monitor the N and K status of the plant at various critical stages of plant development (table 10-1). These recommended levels are a good starting point for monitoring the N status in the Northeast. However, keep in mind that less total N is needed in the Northeast due to the shorter growing season and harvest period.

Boron is a critical element for fruit set and root growth. Boron can be foliar-applied or fertigated as tissue and soil samples indicate. The best way to monitor the actual status of the various nutrients is through regular tissue/petiole testing. Table 10-2 lists the sufficiency ranges for various nutrients for strawberry plants in a plasticulture system.

TABLE 10-1

Sufficiency ranges for fresh petiole sap nitrogen (NO_3–N) and potash (K_2O–K) concentrations (ppm) for strawberry plasticulture at specific stages

DATE/STAGE	NO_3 RANGE	K_2O RANGE
Mid-October	800–900	3,000–3,500
Mid-November	600–800	3,000–3,500
Mid-March	600–800	2,500–3,500
Early April (beginning of bloom)	300–500	2,000–2,500
May 10–June ?? (harvest season)	200–500	1,800–2,500

SOURCE: Hochmuth, G. and E. Albregts. 1994. University of Florida Extension Circular 1141.

TABLE 10-2

Sufficiency range (dry-weight basis) for nutrients in most recently matured whole leaves (tissue analysis—blade plus petiole) for strawberry plasticulture at mid-season

NUTRIENT	ADEQUATE RANGE (%)	NUTRIENT	ADEQUATE NUTRIENT (ppm)
N	2.8–3.0	Fe	50–100
P	0.2–0.4	Mn	25–100
K	1.1–2.5	Zn	20–40
Ca	0.4–1.5	B	20–40
Mg	0.2–0.4	Cu	5–10
S	0.8–1.0	Mo	0.5–0.8

SOURCE: Hochmuth, G. and E. Albregts. 1994. University of Florida Extension Circular 1141.

Bed Preparation

The ultimate goal for the best productivity is a center-crowned, firm bed with tight black plastic. High, wide black-plastic-covered beds promote higher soil temperatures that induce better and more rapid plant development in the fall and spring. They improve water drainage, which decreases root disease problems; improve air movement through foliage for disease prevention; and require less effort (bending and searching) at harvest.

The soil should be worked well and debris removed before making the beds. Bed formation, fertilizer incorporation, fumigation shanking, drip tape installation, and plastic laying can all be done in one step with some equipment. However, in most locations in the Northeast, especially on heavier soils, it is typically better to form the beds with the fertilizer incorporated and then come back and lay the plastic and drip tape.

The plastic must be in direct contact with the soil for efficient soil warming.

Beds 10 inches high and 30–32 inches wide promote the development of large root systems and more branch crowns. Research has shown that wider beds (see section on plant spacing on page 89) allow greater spacing between plant rows, which promotes better sun and air penetration and translates into higher productivity and quality. Beds are spaced as close as possible depending on soil type, tractor size, equipment available, and space needed between rows for pickers; 5-foot row centers are common.

Plastic Mulch

Black plastic mulch keeps the soil warm longer in the fall for improved growth and flower bud initiation, allows the soil to warm quickly in spring for an earlier harvest, keeps fruit clean and disease-free, and controls weeds. Embossed plastic of 1.25-mil thickness is recommended, as it can withstand two or even three strawberry crops under normal conditions (photo 10-2). White-over-black plastic is equally good for retarding weed growth; however, it does not maintain the high soils temperatures in the fall that promote continued root growth. Black plastic is best for inducing the high-value early crop. White-over-black will delay bloom, which may be desirable to avoid spring frosts (and overhead frost protection) or to deliberately delay the crop. Clear plastic is not recommended, because weed control can be a problem, the harvest is delayed (as compared to black plastic), and it can adversely affect the drip tube.

Drip Irrigation

Irrigation is critical to optimal plant development, yield, fruit size, and quality. Drip irrigation is recommended for strawberry plasticulture, as it has multiple applications in the system. As described earlier, it can be used to deliver fumigant directly to the critical area in the bed under the plastic. Drip irrigation is the most efficient way of supplying water directly to the roots without wetting leaves and exacerbating foliage diseases. Applying fertilizer through the drip system (fertigation) is also the most efficient way to deliver nutrients to the plant at the proper time and in the optimal amount without disturbing the plastic. Environmentally friendly practices of producing as many crops as possible with the same plastic mulch and drip tape, combined with proper plastic disposal, are strongly encouraged (see the double-cropping sec-

Photo 10-2. Embossed black plastic mulch and drip irrigation tape being applied in the fall.

tion below and chapter 12, "Managing Used Agricultural Plastics").

The drip tube should always be installed with the emitter holes facing upwards to avoid clogging. It can be laid on the top surface of the bed or buried 1–2 inches deep. Care must be taken not to bury the tube too deep, as water may not wick out to the plants on the far shoulders of the bed, especially on sandy soils. The thickness of drip tube utilized is determined by how many seasons or crops the beds will be used.

Overhead Irrigation

Overhead irrigation (solid-set or microsprinklers) is critical at a few stages in the system. It is helpful during planting and establishment to cool plants and plastic on hot late-summer days and can also be used for evaporative cooling during the harvest season. However, it is imperative to have a dependable solid-set overhead system for frost protection of the early crop (see frost protection section, page 101).

Planting Considerations

Plant Types

Currently, a few plant types are available for the plasticulture system, including plugs, dormant plants, and fresh plants. A fact sheet listing of nurseries that supply plugs and runner tips is listed in the references section (page 135). Always insist on virus-tested plants from a certified nursery when purchasing plants.

Plugs. Transplant "plugs" (figure 10-1, page 97) that are propagated from actively growing runner tips are the current standard for the system. Rooted plugs can be purchased directly from nurseries, or one can purchase tips and root them into plugs (see sidebar, page 96). Plugs are easy to establish, are amenable to mechanical planting, and, as evidenced by research results, give the most consistent yields from season to season. Another benefit is that they are not planted until late August or early September, allowing for summer rotation or double-cropping. Besides high cost, the other limiting factor with plugs has been the limited selection of varieties and date of availability. 'Chandler,' 'Sweet Charlie,' and 'Camarosa' are the only varieties currently available in commercial quantities. Recently, however, nurseries in the mid-Atlantic re-

MAKING PLUGS FROM TIPS

Extended storage of the plantlets or tips is generally not needed. Northern commercial nurseries can harvest fresh tips weekly from early July through mid-October. The tips are shipped by refrigerated truck to the grower's farm for delivery approximately 35 days before field-transplanting. Tips can be stored at 34°F for up to two weeks without deterioration in quality. The boxes, which generally contain approximately 1,000 plantlets, must be stacked "loose" so that cool air can circulate freely around them. The strawberry tips are a living, respiring plant and must be kept cool until you are ready to root them under mist. The cooler should be kept at 75–80% relative humidity. Before rooting, additional plantlet preparation is needed to trim away excess runner cords. An approximately ³⁄₈- to ½-inch runner "stub" serves to anchor the plantlet until new roots develop (see illustrations below). Fresh strawberry tips are best rooted under a fine mist that will wet the foliage yet put very little excess water on the soil. The goal is to keep moisture on the leaves until the plant is well rooted, about seven days. As the roots form, the plants can be weaned from the mist and allowed to get their moisture from the soil. Misting can be gradually reduced over a two- to five-day period. One week after transplanting, it should be possible to pull most plants from the cell and have the root ball remain intact. When that occurs, misting can be stopped.

Strawberry plants raised in containers are grown in specially prepared growing media. Many different media are available, but a soilless medium based on peat, sand, grit, vermiculite, perlite, polystyrene, or other materials is recommended. You will need about 4 cubic feet of media for approximately 1,000 tips in 60-cell rigid plastic trays 2³⁄₈ by 12 by 20 inches. The 60-cell tray is suggested for small- and medium-size strawberry tips. If plantlet lengths of the tips you receive from your supplier are quite variable, it is best to grade the tips into large-, medium-, and small-sized lots. The large tips should be in 50-cell trays, the medium tips in 60-cell trays, and the smaller tips in 72-cell trays. Sticking large tips (longer than 5 inches) in the same tray with small tips (2–3 inches) will result in light competition and irregular root growth of the smaller, shaded tip plants. During misting, shaded tips are susceptible to *Botrytis* infection.

After the misting cycle is complete, trays are moved outside to a fully exposed gravel pad for another two to three weeks of growth and acclimation before they are transplanted to the field. During this final field-conditioning phase, a single daily watering is suggested along with a weekly supplemental drench of a complete fertilizer. A slightly root-bound plug is desirable for mechanical transplanting; plugs for hand-transplanting can be set before this stage is reached. It is not advisable to plant plugs that have been left in the tray for more than five to six weeks.

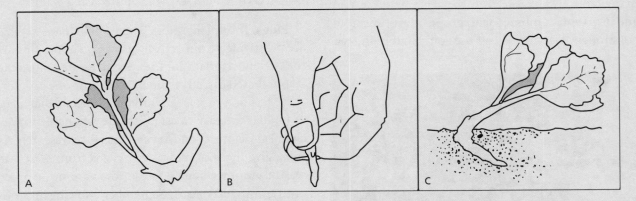

(A) A fresh plantlet used for rooting has one to two expanded leaves with the first root nodules visible. (B) Three-eighths to 0.5 inch of the runner is attached so that it can be inserted in the media to hold the plantlet secure. (C) Side view of the plantlet inserted in a 2³⁄₈-inch plug.

Source: Poling, E. B. and D. W. Monks. 1994.

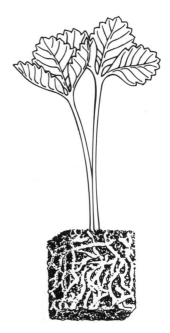

Figure 10-1. Plug plant

gion are concentrating on delivering a larger choice of varieties (including many eastern-adapted varieties) and planting dates (see section below).

Dormant or Frigo Plants. Results of studies in the region show that traditional dormant plants (dormants) may be used in the system. They are less expensive than plugs, offer a larger number of variety choices, and allow for earlier planting. Establishment (planting and deblossoming) is more expensive, as it requires more hand labor. Currently the only way to plant the dormants is by hand; however, a mechanical transplanter that can be adapted to planting dormants is being developed. Also, plant viability can decrease with prolonged storage of the dormants at the nursery, which ultimately reduces plant stands and necessitates costly replanting. Therefore, when ordering plants, be sure to tell the nursery that you will be planting the dormants into a plasticulture system and when the approximate planting date will be. Dormants decrease plant costs and allow for early planting, reducing the overall risk of the system. Therefore, they may play an important role as the system is extended to more limiting northern locations.

Fresh Plants. Fresh plants are the traditional plant type for this system in the Southeast. The plants are grown and shipped just prior to planting, typically in mid-October in Florida. They are less expensive than plugs, but since they are dug bare-root in Canada and shipped, they require special storage, rapid handling, and extended establishment with overhead irrigation (a problem on heavy soils). Variety choice is limited, and they are typically available too late for planting in the Northeast.

An alternative, however, are multiple-crowned "mother plants" (MCF) that are a "byproduct" of the digging and sorting of fresh plants. Two years of investigation revealed that the MCF plants were high-yielding and superior to plugs and fresh single-crown plants when planted on or after the recommended plug planting dates. This plant type can provide for late planting opportunities in northern locations, but availability is limited. MCF plants must be special-ordered from the nursery.

Planting Dates

The optimal planting date for an individual site must be determined to allow ample time to produce sufficient vegetative growth before flower bud initiation. This ensures development of the desired numbers of flower trusses that will result in high yields of quality fruit. Research has shown that the "optimal" planting date can vary from season to season depending on the subsequent fall growing season. Generally, late August through early September seems to be the best range for establishment of plugs in most locations in the mid-Atlantic region (photo 10-3). As you move south to central North Carolina, the planting date is extended

Photo 10-3. Plug-planted strawberries in the fall.

to the first week in October. See table 10-3 for ranges of planting dates for various sites. Plantings that are established later than the optimal planting dates tend to produce fruit earlier the following spring, but yield is generally reduced. In the mid-Atlantic and north, floating row covers applied in October can increase yield and compensate for late plug planting; see section on page 100.

As the system moves north, earlier planting becomes more critical. However, plug availability is currently limited. As improved tip/plug technology fosters plug availability in July or early August, planting plugs in more limiting northern locations will become a reality (see section on future prospects, page 107). Dormants overcome planting-date complications, as they are available spring through summer. However, storage of the plants until the optimal planting dates (late June through mid-July) may reduce plant viability and establishment. MCF plants can have good high yields even when planted up to four weeks later than recommended for plugs. But again, availability is limited.

Cultivars

As with most horticultural crops, variety choice is very important for adaptation, disease resistance, season, and quality. At the core of integrated crop management principles is the utilization of an innate genetic resistance to pests as the most efficient means of control. Utilizing pest-resistant varieties with site-specific adaptation and tolerance to local stresses, including winter cold and summer heat, is always recommended. The plasticulture system is relatively new in the mid-Atlantic and Northeast regions; therefore, it is recommended that growers run their own trials to see what varieties perform best in their location while fitting into their marketing strategy. Varieties that have performed well in matted rows and are popular in the market in your area may be worth trying on plasticulture.

'Chandler' is the current primary cultivar choice for this system, especially for warmer regions. It is one of the most extensively planted varieties worldwide. Developed in California, its high vigor, high productivity, and extended harvest make it well adapted to the system. The fruit are very attractive (symmetrical with good color), have good firmness and shelf life,

TABLE 10-3
Range of planting dates for various sites when establishing strawberry plasticulture plots with plugs, dormants, and fresh plants

PLANT TYPES	WARMER SITES	COLDER SITES
Dormant crowns	Mid- to late July	Mid-June to mid-July
Plugs	Late September to early October	Mid-August to early September
Fresh single crown	Early September	Plants not available
Fresh multiple crown	Early October	Early through late September

and have very good flavor. A major limitation is its susceptibility to anthracnose (*Colletotrichum* species), a disease that infests both plants and fruit. Recently, fungicides to help control the disease have been labeled for use in the Northeast and mid-Atlantic regions. Check with Cooperative Extension in your region to obtain local pest-control recommendations for specifics. As always, starting with certified disease-free plants from a reputable nursery is critical to success.

'Sweet Charlie' is a variety developed in Florida as an early, large, good-flavored berry for the system. It has anthracnose tolerance and is therefore amenable to carryover. It is recommended for warm locations from southern New Jersey and south as an early, high-quality berry to start the season, but it will not yield as high as 'Chandler.' It has not sized well, and blossoms are routinely killed by spring frosts in more northern sites.

'Camarosa' is another variety developed in California for the plasticulture system. The fruit is very large and extra firm and therefore has excellent shelf life. Flavor can be limiting unless berries are harvested dead ripe, which is possible due to the excellent firmness. It is also susceptible to anthracnose. 'Gaviota' has also shown promise in trials in North Carolina and is worthy of trial.

Considerable research on testing eastern-adapted varieties in plasticulture has been conducted with both dormant and plug plants. Many eastern cultivars have proven to be high-yielding, large-fruited, and pest-resistant, and they offer early season extension over 'Chandler.' 'Earliglow' has been extremely early in this system, with a significant portion of its fruit harvested before the other varieties start coming on. Quality has been excellent and size was good. A new release from the New Jersey U.S. Department of Agriculture Breeding Program, 'Avalon,' is early, very large, and has excellent fruit quality. However, yield can suffer when late frosts are common. 'Noreaster' has good productivity and very good fruit size. Flavor is generally good, but it can have a grapey flavor under certain conditions. See table 10-4 for a list of recommended varieties and their performance in the system.

'Allstar' has been a consistently good performer over many years and locations. It is very productive, has large size and good flavor, and is very firm. 'Allstar' is recommended for plasticulture production, especially where it has performed well in matted rows. 'Seneca' has been very productive, with good fruit size and excellent color and firmness, especially in southern New Jersey. Fruit flavor, however, can be less than the high quality that is desirable if the fruit are not picked red ripe. 'Jewel' has performed comparable to 'Seneca,' with slightly better flavor. 'Latestar' has been very high-

yielding with good fruit color in mountain locations. However, fruit size can fall off at the end of the season, and fruit firmness can also be limiting under warm ripening conditions; flavor is also borderline acceptable. 'Marmolada' has consistently been among the highest-yielding varieties. However, the fruit can be very irregular if nitrogen nutrition is insufficient, and flavor can also be limiting for direct fresh market. There is currently a significant breeding effort to develop new varieties that will be adapted to plasticulture in the eastern United States.

Plant Spacing

Late-season, high-density planting (nonrunning) promotes high yields and large fruit size and improves efficiency by promoting fruit production over runner production. The quantity of plants per acre depends on row-center distance [example: 60-inch (5-foot) centers and two rows of plants spaced 12 inches apart with 12 inches between plants in the row = 17,400 plants per acre]. Table 10-5 (page 100) lists required plant numbers per acre for a given spacing between

TABLE 10-4
Recommended strawberry varieties and their performance in plasticulture

VARIETY	SEASON	YIELD	FRUIT SIZE	FIRMNESS	ATTRIBUTES
'Sweet Charlie'	VE	M	M-L[1]	F	Very good flavor; anthracnose tolerance
'Earliglow'	VE	M	S-M	F	Very good flavor
'Avalon' (NJ8826-11)	VE	M	M-L	F	Very good flavor
'Noreaster'	E-M	M-H	M-L	M-F	Productive
'Chandler'	M	VH	M-L	F	Harvests over long season; attractive berry
'Allstar'	M	VH	L	F	Harvests over long season; widely adapted; good sweet flavor
'Camarosa'	M	VH	VL	ExtraF	Good shipping berry; must be full ripe for flavor
'Seneca'	M	VH	L	VF	Attractive berry; very firm—good shipper; ? flavor
'Jewel'	M	H	L	F	Attractive
'Latestar'	M-L	VH[2]	L	M	Very productive; ? flavor
'Marmolada'	M-L	VH[3]	L[3]	F	Very productive

[1]'Sweet Charlie' does not size as well in colder locations.
[2]'Latestar' quality, productivity, and firmness has been best in mountain locations.
[3]'Marmolada' requires a higher nitrogen input (160+ pounds of nitrogen per acre) than other varieties for maximum yield, size, and symmetrical fruit.

KEY:
Season—very early (VE), early (E), midseason (M), late (L).
Yield—medium (M), high (H), very high (VH).
Size—small (S), medium (M), large (L), very large (VL).
Firmness—medium (M), firm (F), very firm (VF), extra firm (extraF).

TABLE 10-5			
Required plant numbers per acre for a given spacing between and within rows			
SPACING WITHIN ROW (inches)	SPACING BETWEEN ROWS (feet)		
	4	5	6
9	32,670	26,136	21,780
12	21,780	17,424	14,520
18	14,520	11,616	9,680

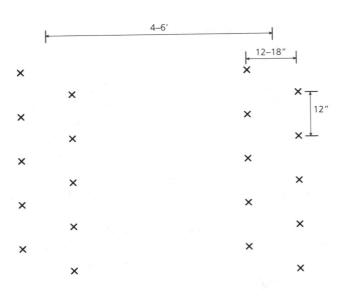

Figure 10-2. Spacing design for plasticulture system

and within rows. Research has shown that 12 inches between plants (staggered double row) is the most efficient in-row spacing for most locations (figure 10-2). However, on fertile soils that induce high vigor, the spacing may be stretched to 18 inches, which saves money on plants. Conversely, when planting later than the recommended planting dates, a tighter density (9 inches) may compensate and maximize yield per acre. Research has also shown that expanding the between-row spacing from 12 to 18 inches can increase yield and quality without increasing plants costs. Care must be taken, however, to ensure that there is still adequate bed width and height for the fruit to hang down without contacting the soil. In general, more space between plants promotes earlier fruiting and decreases disease pressure.

Planting Procedure

Much of the planting of plugs can be mechanized. A mechanical water-wheel transplanter can cut the plastic, make the hole, inject the starter fertilizer, and place the plug. The water wheel can also be used for the initial procedures when planting fresh and dormant plants, except that the actual planting must be done by hand to ensure proper planting depth. As proper planting depth is critical for proper establishment and growth, it is critical to check each plant after setting to ensure proper depth.

Overhead irrigation at planting is desirable to cool plugs and plastic in warm weather and essential for establishment of fresh plants. After initial establishment, if necessary, irrigate through a drip system to continue development. Be careful not to overirrigate through the drip before there is adequate root growth for absorption, as this will lead to wasteful leaching of incorporated nutrients.

Maintenance and Post-Planting Procedures

Maintenance between Rows

The plastic mulch provides an effective barrier against weeds on the raised beds. Some hand weeding may be needed in the planting holes, especially on non-fumigated beds. Clean cultivation or turf can be used for between-the-row maintenance. The overwhelming majority in the mid-Atlantic region use clean cultivation with preemergence herbicides. Herbicides, straw mulch, cultivation, or a combination of these can be used to maintain the vegetation-free strip. Contact the county Cooperative Extension office for local commercial strawberry weed-management recommendations. When cultivating, care must be taken not to hit the plastic bed sides or pull up the plastic that is under the soil.

Many growers in the Southeast choose to establish a sod strip between rows. In North Carolina and hill sites where erosion may be a problem, ryegrass is seeded (at 15–20 pounds per acre) between the rows prior to planting and then killed back in the early winter. This can be advantageous for erosion control and provides a stable base during wet springs.

Row Covers

Spunbonded polyester or polypropylene floating row covers (FRC) are an integral part of the strawberry plasticulture system and a necessity for optimal production in the mid-Atlantic region (photo 10-4). FRC increase establishment costs but serve multiple beneficial roles in development and production, which more than covers the added costs. FRC promote higher temperatures under the covers, which is desirable for many reasons. When applied in mid-October (when average daily air temperatures are in the low 70s), the elevated temperatures continue plant development and branch crown formation and promote flower bud initiation, resulting in higher yields. The FRC warm the beds early in the spring, inducing earlier fruiting when the value of the crop is typically the highest (see harvest considerations, page 103). Also in the spring, row covers maintain higher temperatures during the day and night, which in many cases is adequate to protect from frost without overhead sprinklers (see frost protection below). The planting can be uncovered and re-covered depending on the specific temperatures expected.

FRC reduce wind desiccation, protect the plantings from rapid changes in temperature, and provide buffering from extremes in temperature. Uncovered plantings have experienced extensive deer predation in the fall and winter. Covers over the green plants tend to deter the deer. FRC also seem to protect the planting from tarnished plant bug and strawberry clipper damage through earlier bloom and physical exclusion.

The covers may be utilized a second and even third season when heavier materials (0.9–1.4 ounces per square yard) are purchased initially. The heavier materials are more expensive but are more efficient and can be utilized for multiple years, which reduces their overall annual cost per acre. When applying the covers, it is preferable to hold down one side permanently with soil or other material and the opposite side with something more temporary (such as irrigation pipe, bricks, or UV-stable sandbags) so that the field can be uncovered and re-covered in the spring if there are late frost warnings. Remove the FRC at the first signs of bloom to allow for bee pollination. Leaving the covers on for too long into bloom may reduce fruit size and reduce light transmission to the leaves.

Straw Mulch

As the system moves north into climates with colder winters (Massachusetts to Ontario), growers have found success with straw mulch as winter protection instead of or in addition to the floating row covers (FRC). The straw is applied when the plants are dormant, as with the traditional matted row. Advantages of using straw are the low cost compared to FRC and the additional winter cold insulation. Straw-covered beds are not subjected to the extensive fluctuations in temperature that can occur with FRC during warm sunny days in January and February. Drawbacks of using straw instead of FRC are the losses of the additional growth and flower bud initiation in the fall, the induction of the earlier crop in the spring, and late frost protection provided by the option of re-covering with the FRC. It is also sometimes difficult to keep a thick enough straw layer on the plastic-mulch-covered raised beds.

The crop can still be staggered somewhat when using straw. To induce an earlier bloom, the straw is removed completely from the plants and bed in the early spring to expose the black plastic and warm the bed. If the bloom is to be delayed, the straw is removed only from above the plant itself and left on the bed to prevent sun penetration to the black plastic.

Frost Protection

Strawberry flower buds are susceptible to frost injury any time after bud break and must be protected if the fruit is to develop. Open strawberry flowers are more prone to freeze damage than green fruit, and green fruit are more sensitive than ripe fruit (table 10-6).

W. J. Lamont

Photo 10-4. Spunbonded row cover over fall-planted strawberries is an integral part of the strawberry plasticulture system.

TABLE 10-6
Critical temperatures (air) for strawberry buds, flowers, and fruit

BUDS EMERGE	BUDS CLOSED	FLOWERS OPEN	SMALL GREEN FRUIT
10°F	22°–27°F	30°F	28°F

SOURCE: Funt et al., 1985
NOTE: Duration of temperature for damage can be 20 minutes to 2 hours, depending on wind, humidity, and cultivar.

Many factors influence the actual damage, including the stage of development, position of blossom, severity/duration of the freeze, wind speed, cloud cover, and surface moisture.

Irrigation

Overhead irrigation is the usual method for freeze protection. The irrigation water provides heat to the plant as the water temperature drops to 32°F and especially as it freezes. As long as the temperature of the flower or fruit stays above 31°F, no damage results (see table 10-6). The lower the air temperature, the greater the amount of water is needed to maintain the temperature of the flowers and fruit above the damaging level (table 10-7). However, if wind speed is 8–10 miles per hour or greater, water application with this technique can be erratic, and plants can be severely damaged. WARNING: The use of overhead irrigation for frost protection is a sensitive procedure that could result in **major plant damage** if not handled properly. See the references section, page 135, for more information.

TABLE 10-7
Inches of water/hour to apply to prevent freezing, with wind speed and air temperature considered

AIR TEMPERATURE (°F at canopy)	WIND SPEED (mph)				
	0–1	2–4	5–8	10–14	18–22
27	0.10	0.10	0.10	0.10	0.20
24	0.10	0.16	0.30	0.40	0.80
20	0.16	0.30	0.60	0.80	—
18	0.20	0.40	0.70	1.00	—

SOURCE: Martsoff and Gerber, The Pennsylvania State University

Thermometers should be calibrated in an ice bath and placed in the lowest spot(s) in the field, fully exposed to the sky and just above the mulch (be sure they are not protected by plants). The most accurate way to monitor temperatures under the covers and/or ice is to install thermocouples into the flowers that can be read externally with a digital thermometer without disturbing the cover. This way, one can determine more accurately when to turn the water on as the temperature drops and when to turn the water off when the ice is melting.

In general, when used without floating row covers, sprinklers are turned on at 34°F (a higher temperature if the dew point is very low) and not turned off until the ice begins to melt and continues to melt when no additional irrigation is applied. Remember, turning off the sprinklers too early can result in evaporative cooling that can cause severe damage to the planting.

Row Covers

As mentioned previously, spunbonded floating row covers (FRC) offer two major benefits in frost protection. Growers utilizing FRC will realize several (2–4) degrees of protection just from the covers, especially with residual heat buildup under the covers. On many nights, these few extra degrees can be enough to avoid irrigation. Row covers should be reapplied early in the day to trap latent ground heat whenever an overnight frost/freeze is anticipated.

When more severe frost/freezes are anticipated, supplemental overhead irrigation can be applied directly over the covers. Irrigation applied over the covers is more effective and less risky than irrigation on exposed plants, as it is easier to maintain an even ice coating over the FRC. When using irrigation over FRC with thermocouples to monitor, the sprinklers do not need to be turned on until the blossom temperature under the cover has dropped to 31°F. The water can be turned off as soon as the blossom temperature under the cover rises to 31°F. If temperatures permit, remove the FRC soon after irrigation to allow for drying and pollination.

Pest Control

The plasticulture system is based on integrated crop management principles and practices that avoid and/

or reduce pest pressure. Late-summer planting affords relief from the heat, drought, weed, and disease pressures of mid-summer. The system decreases the dependency on chemical pesticides by maintaining a microclimate that is not conducive to pest development and by physically excluding pests from the susceptible plant material.

Black plastic mulch can eliminate or reduce the need for herbicides and fumigation against weeds, since it blocks the light needed for weed seed germination and development. The raised bed and black plastic mulch decrease disease pressure by keeping the fruit cleaner and drier, decreasing *Botrytis* fruit rot and leather rot and increasing shelf life. The raised bed allows greater air movement through the vegetative canopy, promoting quicker drying of morning dew and rainfall, thereby reducing the duration of disease-promoting conditions on leaves and fruit. The beds also allow the soil to drain more efficiently, reducing or eliminating root diseases such as red stele, black root rot, and *Verticillium* wilt.

Plants are in the field for only a short period of time in the annual system, which avoids many pest problems, since plants have fewer chances to be exposed to pests. Plant trash is greatly reduced, as leaves are much younger. This greatly decreases the inoculum source for gray mold *(Botrytis)*, other fruit rots, and leaf spots. Leaf-spot cover sprays in the fall are typically not needed, as the growth is much younger and has not been exposed to inoculum during the heat of the summer.

Floating row covers (FRC) aid in avoiding insect infestations by physically excluding pests such as tarnished plant bug. Since the FRC promote an earlier crop, they also serve to accelerate plant development past the susceptible stage before pests such as the strawberry clipper emerge. However, the increased heat under the FRC in the dormant season has increased aphid and mite pressure. It is important to scout for mites and aphids and treat when necessary before applying the cover and immediately after removing it in the spring. Root weevils have not been a pest in this system, since plants are in the field for only one or two seasons. Sap beetles are very rarely found in first-year beds with this system and are greatly reduced relative to matted rows in second-year fields. Again, contact your Cooperative Extension office for local commercial strawberry pest-management recommendations.

Pythium and *Rhizoctonia,* which can come in on transplants, can be more of a problem on fumigated soils, possibly due to a lack of competing microorganisms. Starting with healthy transplants from a reputable certified nursery is of great importance to avoid problems. When rooting tips to make plugs, be careful to avoid overwatering in the propagation bed.

If beds are carried over for a second growing season, the traditional strawberry pests can become more of a problem. Anthracnose, which is typically a problem in warmer southern climates, can be a major disease problem in this system, especially in carryover beds. Again, always start with disease-free tips and plugs, preferably greenhouse-produced or from a northern nursery. Also, be sure to remove the old leaves *and fruit* from the field during renovation to reduce disease inoculum.

Harvest Considerations

The raised bed, black plastic, and floating row covers (FRC) all work together to advance bloom and harvest. Warm sunny springs can induce up to one-month-earlier harvests than traditional matted rows. This can be advantageous, since the early fruit can typically command the highest value at the market. Strawberries are one of the earliest crops of the season, so an early harvest can be used to get early cash flow. The down side is that early bloom means increased risk of frost damage and greater need for frost protection.

Conversely, to avoid an early crop, avoid irrigation for frost protection, or promote a later harvest, remove the FRC early (just as growth begins in the spring).

DEER

The fresh, tender green leaves present fall through spring make deer grazing a major problem in this system. If the leaves are mowed off by deer in the fall/winter, yield will be reduced the following season. Many of the techniques used to protect other crops, including fencing (exclusion and electrified), fenced-in dogs, audio scare devices, repellants, and harvest, are viable options.

Research in northern New Jersey has shown that bloom and harvest can be delayed up to two weeks by removing the FRC early. However, yield was also down when the covers were removed early. Care must be taken to put the cover back on if the temperatures are going to dip low enough to cause damage to vegetative parts of the plants (see table 10-6 on page 102). Early cover removal can also be used to stagger the harvest by removing the cover from a portion of the field.

Total production, timing of first harvest, and length of harvest can vary from season to season, depending on the growing conditions from planting until bloom. Also, it is sometimes desirable to estimate the timing and amount of harvest for marketing purposes. By monitoring plant development, it is possible to estimate yield and date of first harvest to notify potential markets and maximize profits (see the references section, page 135, for more information). The duration from bloom to harvest is approximately 30 days, depending on conditions. In southern regions, frost protection is initiated about 30 days prior to when the first harvest is desired.

Harvest begins earlier on plasticulture than matted rows, and staggering the harvest with a succession of varieties is possible. 'Sweet Charlie' is the earliest of the standard varieties. 'Earliglow' and 'Avalon' are also very early on plastic. The relative harvest season for varieties on matted rows is about the same in plasticulture.

An interesting difference between matted rows and plasticulture is the duration of harvest. 'Chandler' on plastic will typically be harvested for about four to five weeks; six weeks is possible in cool seasons. 'Chandler' and 'Sweet Charlie' are prone to "second peaks" of harvest, where a few days after the bulk of the harvest is over, there is an additional flush of large ripe fruit from secondary branch crowns.

The early, large, clean, high-quality, local fruit has commanded premium prices at wholesale and direct retail markets. This high return has been helpful to cover not only the high establishment costs, but to give a significant return per acre (see the economics section on page 105). The ease of harvest of the individual plants on high plastic beds reduces harvest costs and improves efficiency. This also allows the harvest to take place early in the morning, when temperatures are still cool, which is best for quality and shelf life. Harvesting shortly after a rain is feasible with plasticulture, as the beds and fruit dry out quickly.

Harvesting early when the fruit is still cool coupled with rapid removal of field heat will maximize the shelf life of strawberries. Forced-air cooling is the quickest and most efficient way to remove the majority of the field heat. Once cooled, the flats can be stacked until the fruit is marketed. If the fruit is to be sold direct retail, it is best to pick only what is to be sold that day. Again, if the fruit is picked while still cool, it does not need to be refrigerated, as the fruit may loose their sheen if cooled and warmed.

The high yields also make u-pick a lucrative option; however, once customers get accustomed to the ease of harvesting on raised beds with plastic, it is difficult to get them to pick on the matted row. Many growers are using their first-year fields for wholesale or direct retail and allowing u-pick on the renovated second-year fields.

Renovation and Vegetable Double-Cropping

Plasticulture establishment costs are high, so research has been conducted to investigate options for a second year of strawberry production and/or double-cropping with vegetables. These options make optimal use of the beds, plastic, fertility, and drip tape by producing a second crop reusing all of the original inputs. Triple-cropping experiments are also being investigated. The following are considerations and techniques for the various alternatives.

University research as well as commercial grower experience has shown that both second-year cropping of berries and vegetable double-cropping can be profitable if handled properly. Which option employed should be determined by the overall crop-production and marketing strategies employed in the operation.

Renovated "carryover" strawberry beds can be very high-yielding, however, there is usually a decrease in average fruit size that may limit marketing options. This is especially true of first-year beds that have produced a high yield due to high branch crown density. First-year beds that have not produced the high yields that are expected for the system are best suited for second-year production, since the plants are not as large and dense. Second-year beds, however, have an increased risk of diseases and pests, especially anthracnose and sap beetles. 'Sweet Charlie' is a better choice for renovation than 'Chandler' because of the risk of anthracnose. Carrying over beds has economic advantages, but many of the advantages of the annual plasticulture system are lost, as typically pest populations can build up and cause more damage in the second season.

Double-cropping of vegetables in the same season as the strawberry harvest can be very profitable, as long as the proper choice of crops is made as determined by the remaining length and conditions of the growing season. As always, one should always know the specific cultural practices and market demand before planting any crop.

Renovation Techniques for Second-Year Production

Soon after the strawberry harvest has ended, mow the leaves to stimulate healthy new growth. Cut the leaves as low as possible without damaging or pulling up the crowns or damaging the plastic. It is important to remove the old leaves and fruit from the field to reduce disease inoculum.

Fields that have had high production during the first fruiting season tend to have high branch crown numbers (five to eight) and will benefit from crown-thinning. Crown-thinning is accomplished after mowing by inserting an asparagus knife or sharp object through the center of the crown and removing about half, being careful to avoid damaging the remaining section and roots.

It is important that beds are drip-irrigated throughout the heat of the summer. However, it is best to hold back fertilizer applications to limit regrowth unless plants show stress or deficiency. Fertigation of 20–30 pounds of actual nitrogen is applied in late August or early September.

The plastic mulch will continue to provide an effective barrier from weeds on the raised beds for the second crop, provided it was not substantially damaged during the first season. For between-row weed control, cultivation, straw, or herbicides can be used; as always, contact your local Cooperative Extension office for commercial strawberry pest-control recommendations. **Remember, herbicides should never be sprayed over the mulched beds, as runoff into holes will greatly increase the actual application rate.**

Second-year beds do not need early-applied floating row covers like first-year plantings. To keep costs down, many commercial growers in southern New Jersey, where the winters are milder, do not cover the renovated plantings at all over the second winter, while others utilize the "used" covers from the previous season. The high first-year inputs coupled with very little input necessary for a second year of harvest has prompted many growers to carry over their beds. Some growers have even been successful in keeping the fields for a third season.

Techniques for Vegetable Double-Cropping

Soon after fruiting, the strawberry plants are killed with two consecutive sprays (spaced two to three days apart) of a contact herbicide. Dead plants are left in place to retard weed growth in the holes and keep the bed intact. It is best to wait for some rain before planting to prevent problems from herbicide residue on the plastic bed.

The timing of the strawberry harvest can be important when deciding which vegetable to double-crop, especially in locations with short growing seasons. In seasons when the strawberry harvest finishes early, long-season crops such as tomatoes, peppers, melons, and pumpkins are a viable option. In seasons when the strawberry harvest ends late, short- and/or cool-season crops such as squashes, beans, greens, and cole crops (broccoli, cauliflower, cabbage, collards, and Brussels sprouts as transplants) are the preferred candidates. Herbs and cut flowers could also be viable options. Success with each crop requires care as to the specific requirements for spacing, water, nutrients, and pest control for that crop. Again, see the local commercial production recommendations for details.

Economics

The plasticulture strawberry production system has shown consistently high commercial profitability in the Southeast and mid-Atlantic regions. The system costs more initially and overall than the traditional matted-row system. However, harvest costs are reduced and productivity is typically higher, therefore bottom-line profitability has been higher. Plasticulture establishment inputs range from $5,000 to $7,000 per acre, while matted-row costs are typically $2,500–$4,500 per acre. Commercial yields range from 10,000 to 22,000 pounds per acre for plasticulture (4,000–12,000 pounds per acre for matted rows). In addition, the excellent fruit size and very high-quality plasticulture fruit commands a higher price. The plasticulture berries are being sold for $1.75 to $3.75 per quart; on the average, this is 25–40% higher than berries grown in matted rows. If a commercial grower harvests 15,000 pounds per acre, sells the fruit for $2.00 per pound, and incurs $13,362 in expenses (includ-

ing harvest), *the net is about $16,638 per acre.* An average matted-row scenario of 10,000 pounds per acre at $1.33 with $7,811 in expenses equals *$5,489 per acre net* (see the detailed economic summary in table 10-8). With this scenario, *plasticulture profitability is 300% higher* ($16,637–$5,489), not including the potential profits from vegetable double-cropping. This profitability makes strawberry plasticulture one of the most profitable crops on a per-acre basis. Obviously, actual differences will depend on production and market price at specific locations.

Although the majority of the fruit is sold direct retail for the highest margin, a few commercial growers in southern New Jersey have worked their fruit into

TABLE 10-8
Economic summary of plasticulture production and marketing

OPERATION (Year 1)	AMOUNT	UNIT	COST ($)	OPERATION (Year 1)	AMOUNT	UNIT	COST ($)
Plow			35.00	Hand-weeding/ labor	2	hour	12.00
Disc/harrow			15.00	Pesticides (5x)			
Lime	2	ton	50.00	Thiodan 3EC	1.3	quart	11.70
				Captan 50WP	9	pound	22.50
Fertilizer				Benlate 50WP	1	pound	16.00
10-10-10	300	pound	39.00	Rovral 50WP	2	pound	40.00
Ammonium nitrate	100	pound	10.00	Kelthane 4EC	1	quart	50.00
Labor/machine	0.3	hour	7.46	Labor/machine	2.5	hour	64.38
Form beds	2	hour	82.92	Frost protection (water)		hour	0.00
Herbicide (at planting)				Frost protection (FRC)[1]	6	hour	36.00
Sinbar 80WP	4	ounce	6.40	Remove FRC and store[1]	4	hour	24.00
Devrinol 50WP	3	pound	27.00	Irrigation	20	hour	322.40
Labor/machine	1	hour	25.75				
Plastic			174.24	Harvest/labor (pounds/hour)[2]	30		3,000.00
Drip tape			191.66	Quart/16-ounce container[3]	15,000		3,000.00
Fumigation				8-quart carriers	1,875		1,406.25
Vapam through drip	50	gram	500.00	Yield (pounds)			15,000
Custom—labor/machine	2.5	hour	40.30	Total expenses			13,362.48
Planting				Average price/pound			2.00
Plants	17,424		2,613.60				
Labor/machine	8	hour	244.16	Total income			30,000.00
Irrigation	8	hour	128.96	Net income			16,637.52
Install row cover							
Material			1,089.00				
Labor	4	hour	24.00				
Fertilizer							
Liquid fertilizer	10	gram	12.50				
Labor/machine	2.5	hour	40.30				

[1] FRC = floating row cover

[2] Harvest costs assume 40% increase in picking efficiency with plasticulture system.

[3] Matted-row berries are marketed in pulp quarts, plasticulture in 16-ounce clamshells.

the large commercial supermarket chains in the area. They are successfully competing with California berries due to the superior quality and the high demand and margin for local produce. The value of the fruit has been even higher in the more northern New Jersey locations, and that has helped to more rapidly spread the system to those areas. There are also a few organic growers in the mid-Atlantic region who are using the plasticulture system and marketing the fruit for between $2.00 and $3.75 per pint. This system has great potential for organic production, as described in the nutrition and pest control sections (see pages 92 and 102).

Future Prospects

Development of a Local Tip Nursery Industry to Support Plasticulture

The demand for plugs of the eastern varieties has fostered the development of a new nursery industry in the mid-Atlantic region, including both field and greenhouse tip production. Production of tips for plugs in the greenhouse will permit better control of production, allow earlier planting for northern locations, greatly reduce disease risks, and increase variety choices. Establishing a plug nursery (to go along with the strong existing dormant industry) that can "insure" plant/variety availability in the region will expedite the expansion of the production system within the region.

Breeding Specifically for Plasticulture

Development of varieties that are regionally adapted and have the vegetative and reproductive traits that are optimal for production in the system is the next step to increase production efficiency. A cooperative breeding program (based in Maryland) has been established to breed strawberry varieties specifically for the system (covering Florida to New York). Unique and diverse germplasm has been obtained that contains traits to be incorporated that could make the system completely pesticide-free and significantly extend the geographic range and seasons of production. Existing programs in Florida and North Carolina are currently breeding specifically for plasticulture, and the U.S. Department of Agriculture Strawberry Breed-

ing Program in Beltsville, Maryland, also tests many selections on plastic.

Additional Research and Extension

The plasticulture system has shown good profitability and great potential in many sections of the United States. Research and extension programs have opened the door to new and exciting opportunities to improve productivity and decrease costs. Studies utilizing hoops over the beds with floating row covers show multiple advantages: uniform plant development and fruiting; extension of the flower bud initiation period in the fall; added protection from the adverse winter environment; greater protection against frost/freeze damage; and season extension through earlier fruiting when the prices are the best. University and commercial experiments with "high tunnels" in Pennsylvania and New England take that concept even further for season extension. Also, as more commercial growers are maintaining planting for a second fruiting season, research is needed to determine the best renovation practices, including mowing, crown-thinning, fertilization, and disease monitoring and control.

Summary

High-density strawberry plasticulture production systems can have increased profitability over conventional matted-row plantings. This system is rapidly expanding in the mid-Atlantic and Northeast regions; however, it is best to start with small acreage and increase as knowledge and experience increases. Additional investigations into varieties, planting dates, microclimate, and so forth, are being conducted to broaden the adaptation and decrease the potential "risk" of the system.

Acknowledgments

The author would like to acknowledge Robert Rouse (University of Maryland Cooperative Extension), Barclay Poling (North Carolina State University), Charlie O'Dell (Virginia Tech Cooperative Extension), and, from Rutgers Cooperative Extension, Steve Garrison, Pete Nitzsche, and Pete Probasco for their input into this chapter.

CHAPTER 11

Specialty Cut Flower Plasticulture

Robert D. Berghage and James Sellmer

There is a long history of plasticulture in cut-flower production in the United States. Cut flowers were some of the first crops grown in plastic-covered greenhouses as older glass hothouses were replaced or re-covered.

Unfortunately, much of the large-scale production of cut flowers has moved from the United States to Central and South America in the last two to three decades. This shift has occurred for a number of reasons. The dominant factors have been labor costs and inexpensive and reliable shipping. Cheap labor in Latin America has made U.S. production noncompetitive, particularly with standard cut flowers that have relatively long postharvest life spans and are easy to ship. Traditional standbys of the florist industry such as carnations and chrysanthemums are almost exclusively imported. There is still significant greenhouse rose production in parts of the United States, but these greenhouses are under pressure from overseas, too, and production is decreasing.

This negative outlook for commercial production of traditional cut flowers does not, however, carry over into the niche market production of specialty cut flowers. Specialty cut flowers are cut flowers that are used in smaller quantities, are difficult to produce or ship, or have limited postharvest longevity. The production of these flowers has increased in recent years, and there is a great deal of interest in their production as an alternative to, or complement to, traditional farm products. Many small Mennonite farms in Pennsylvania, for example, have started production of specialty cut flowers as a supplement to help offset low prices received for their staple commodities. Most of this specialty cut-flower production is in the field rather than the greenhouse.

One of the most successful options for field production of specialty cut flowers is the use of a plasticulture system adapted from vegetable production systems (photos 11-1 and 11-2). Raised beds, plastic mulch, and drip irrigation are used. The plastic mulch helps to control weeds, greatly reducing labor requirements and increasing yield and quality. The mulch also helps to keep the flowers clean, reduces water loss from evaporation, and can warm the soil in the spring for earlier harvests. Drip irrigation reduces labor, conserves water, improves flower quality because of more uniform water application, and, when coupled with a fertilizer injection system, can improve fertilization practices.

Some specialty cut-flower producers have returned to the greenhouse or unheated cold frames (high tunnels). Production in an enclosed or partially enclosed structure provides numerous benefits in improved quality, since flowers are protected from adverse weather conditions and foraging wildlife. The combination of inexpensive weather protection with high

Photo 11-1. Production of specialty cut flowers using plasticulture for the local marketplace.

Photo 11-2. Sunflower crop in raised beds with plastic mulch and drip irrigation.

tunnels, and the plastic mulch/raised bed production system, is offering some producers a low-cost, high-quality system for raising specialty cut flowers.

Cut flowers are a specialty crop well suited to small-scale and part-time farming operations. Increasing demand for a wide variety of fresh-cut flowers has kept this market growing, but producing fresh-cut flowers is not for everyone. They have special production requirements and a fairly short shelf life, and there is a relatively short field-growing and marketing season in the mid-Atlantic and Northeast.

Plasticulture Production Considerations

Site Selection

Most cut flowers prefer a well-drained site with soils free from agricultural herbicide residues. Deep fertile soils will greatly simplify the process of developing the site, but soils can be improved through cover cropping, the application of composts or manure, and other soil-building practices. Preplant soil testing is highly recommended. Preplant fertilization without soil testing is just a guess. Too much fertilizer is not only a waste of money; it may lead to toxic buildup in the soil and environmental contamination. For example, it is not uncommon to see phosphorus buildup in soils fertilized for several years with complete blended fertilizers. When this occurs, the grower

should switch to a low- or no-phosphorus fertilizer. The use of plastic mulch can help to reduce the leaching of fertilizer, particularly from sandy soils during periods of heavy rain. This can be a great benefit in reducing the potential for environmental contamination. It is also important to test the pH of the soil. Nutrient availability is restricted at high pH, while at low pH, toxic levels of some minor nutrients may occur. The optimum soil pH range for cut-flower production lies between 5.5 and 7.5. Getting transplants and seedlings off to a good start is critical to a high-yield, high-quality crop.

Bed Preparation

Raised beds are fast becoming a standard practice in growing high-value cut flowers. The benefits of raised beds include: earlier crops, because the sun can heat beds on the sides as well as the top; increased production and improved soil drainage from increased depth of the topsoil; and decreased weed pressure and simplified fertilizer application when raised beds are used with plastic mulch.

Appropriate bed size is influenced by the market and the site. Bed length for "cut-your-own" production should be much shorter than in other commercial production systems. Customers should not be expected to navigate much more than about 25 feet of bed. In addition, space between beds in these production/marketing systems should be large enough to provide easy access and should be planted to turf. For most other commercial production systems, bed length should be limited by the distance workers carry the harvested crop. A reasonable distance for a worker to carry the harvested flowers is 50–75 feet. If beds can be reached from both ends, this translates to a bed length of 100–150 feet. The width of the bed is limited by the workers' ability to reach in to cut the flowers. Bed width should be limited to 4 feet or less, since a worker cannot cut and remove flowers more than 2 feet into the bed without damaging the rest of the crop. The space between beds should be determined by the approach to weed control. If necessary, bed spacing should provide adequate space for tillage equipment to be used without damaging the crop.

The same equipment used in vegetable production for shaping beds and laying plastic mulch and drip irrigation can be used for cut-flower production. Plastic mulch color does not seem to have much effect on quality or yield of cut flowers. Sunflower, celosia, cosmos, and strawflower grown with silver, red, white, or black plastic mulch had similar yields and quality ratings in trials at The Pennsylvania State University. Mulch selection should thus depend on cost and durability. Some specialty cut flowers are herbaceous perennials or woody shrubs. It may be desirable with these perennial crops to have mulch that will survive two or more seasons in the field. This can help the plants become well established so they can fill the bed to limit weed growth before the mulch either breaks down or must be removed. Consider, however, that the mulch may also limit the growth and spread of some perennials in the bed, so care must be exercised with long-lasting mulch materials and plants that spread with rhizomes.

Irrigation Systems

Drip irrigation is a critical component of the cut-flower plasticulture production system. The high value and high quality requirements of a specialty cut-flower production system demand supplemental irrigation to maximize profitability. Overhead irrigation is not a good option because of potential for direct foliar and flower damage and increased disease problems. Specialty cut flowers require more water than many other field crops, and yields may be reduced to uneconomical levels without supplemental irrigation. Plastic mulch limits water loss to evaporation and provides for more uniform, consistent soil moisture content. Typical drip irrigation systems include a back-flow preventer, an injector to allow fertilizer additions, drip tape, and a central or distributed header system. Drip tape typically has 6- to 12-inch emitter perforation spacing. The desired spacing depends on the crop and the soil. In a coarse-textured soil with good drainage, closer spacing will be required than in a fine-textured soil. For woody plants and larger herbaceous perennials, a point-source emitter system may be used. Individual emitters, one or two per plant, are attached to a polyethylene supply line, often with small-diameter supply tubes. Individual emitters typically deliver between $1/2$ and 2 gallons per hour. Rodents may chew through the small polyethylene supply tubes if they are exposed. If this is a problem, it may be necessary to cover the whole system with mulch. System design must consider slopes and water pressure. Design guidelines can be obtained from any of the suppliers of commercial irrigation supplies. See chapter 3 of this manual for more information.

Water quality is an important consideration in the management of the irrigation system in cut-flower plasticulture production. High-alkalinity water is common in much of the mid-Atlantic. Calcium and other minerals can form a "lime" crust in the openings of emitters, reducing water flow and effectively plugging them over time. Adding acid to the water or an acid pulse through the injection system at the end of each irrigation can often reduce this problem.

WARNING! Always add acid to water slowly. Never add water to acid—the reaction could cause splattering.

Planting

Most field-grown cut flowers are best started from transplants or plugs, although direct-seeding can also be a successful strategy. Plant spacing in the field varies among species and sometimes between individual cultivars. Denser plant spacing generally increases yield of annual cut flowers. Many annuals can be planted with a 6- to 8-inch spacing within the row and 12–14 inches between rows. Although denser spacing may increase yield, it also results in a thick leaf canopy and increased disease in some plants. Plants susceptible to mildew and *Botrytis* may need greater spacing to increase air movement in the plant canopy. Some vigorous massive plants like cosmos may need additional space as well. Cosmos and similar plants should be planted on 12-inch centers in the row with 18 inches between rows. Perennials and woody plants may need even greater spacing depending on growth habit and lifespan. Some woody shrubs may need as much as 4 feet between plants. The spacing of perennials also depends on how long they are to be grown in the bed. Yarrow, for example, should be divided and replanted every two to three years to maintain optimum production; thus, it can be planted closer together than peonies, which should be divided every ten years. Annual cut flowers are typically planted in a double row in the bed with the irrigation tape down the center. Perennial woodies and vigorous annuals may be planted in a single row in each bed. The irrigation tape is offset to one side when a single-row planting is used to avoid damaging the irrigation tape when planting. Most new growers plant by hand, but mechanical transplanting can greatly simplify and speed this process. Vegetable plug planters can easily do double duty to plant cut flowers as well.

Wind Protection and Support

Field-grown cut flowers can be easily damaged by strong winds. Protection can be accomplished by carefully selecting the site and using well-designed windbreaks or by growing plants in high tunnels. Windbreaks can be made up of live plants, fencing materials such as split bamboo, or plastic shade fabric. The effectiveness of a windbreak diminishes with distance from the crop. See chapter 6 for more information on windbreaks.

Some cut flowers require support as well. Several wide-mesh plastic products are available. See appendix A (page 123) for more information. These products provide a grid of support for the flowers that encourages straight stems and upright growth. Plastic mesh used for cut-flower support has a 4- to 6-inch grid. It is rolled out over the crop and then supported above the bed with metal or wood posts. The plastic grid is applied at planting and raised with the crop as it grows. The mesh can be used for more than one year; however, it is often damaged during harvest, which may limit reuse. The plastic support grid can greatly improve quality of plants that need support to develop straight stems. It should, however, not be used on all plants, as it can greatly impede harvesting. Similar wire mesh products made from welded wire are also available.

High Tunnels, Cold Frames, and Greenhouses

There is renewed interest in producing specialty cut flowers in heated and unheated greenhouse structures. Commercial field cut-flower growers have become interested in the use of high tunnels and cold frames to lengthen the growing season, providing both earlier harvests in the spring and extending the season into the fall. Research is currently underway to determine the suitability of different structures and specialty crops for these production systems (photo 11-3). Some traditional field-grown cut flowers have potential for greenhouse production. Sunflower, for ex-

Photo 11-3. Sunflower crop in a high tunnel.

ample, can be forced in small containers in the greenhouse. Crop time totals ten weeks. This production system is sometimes called "quick cropping." The general concept is to produce the cut flower in a small container under optimal greenhouse conditions. After the flower is cut, the container and plant are discarded and a new plant is started. Other potential "quick crop" cut flowers for greenhouse production include ageratum, carthamus, celosia, cosmos, and matthiola.

Pest Control

Many different plants that attract a wide variety of pests can be used for cut flowers. When possible, select cultivars that are relatively pest-free. Keep careful records and conduct frequent scoutings to detect pest problems early. Recognizing pest, disease, nutritional, and cultural problems early will usually make controlling them easier and less costly. Many pest problems can be avoided entirely with good sanitation and the use of simple cultural techniques such as crop rotation.

Insects. While many insects inhabit flower plantings, only a few are recognized as economically significant. Aphids, thrips, spider mites, leafhoppers, beetles, and caterpillars are common problems in many flower plantings. Biological, biorational, and more traditional chemical controls are available. Pest populations can often be controlled by naturally occurring parasites and predators. Cover spray pesticides with long residuals should be avoided to protect predator populations. Beneficial insects such as lacewings can also be purchased from biological control companies. Biorational controls include horticultural oils, insecticidal soaps, and extracts of neem oil. These typically have short residuals and minimal impact on beneficial organisms. It may also be necessary to use synthetic chemicals for insect control at times. Always use products labeled specifically for the use you intend, and look for materials that have the lowest toxicity to bees.

Diseases. Fungal diseases can have a major impact on a cut-flower planting. While many do not kill the flowers, they can drastically reduce the salability. Common problems include powdery mildew, damping-off, *Botrytis*, leaf spots, several viruses, and aster yellows. Practicing good crop rotations, carefully selecting cultivars, maintaining optimal growing conditions, and keeping weeds and insects under control will significantly reduce the incidence of diseases. The plasticulture system is specifically intended to reduce disease and weed problems. Disease incidence is reduced because plants are kept cleaner. Soil splashing onto the plant during rain is often a source of fungal spores of *Rhizoctonia* and other plant pathogens. Drip irrigation helps to reduce disease by reducing the wetting of foliage, and raised beds improve drainage, resulting in reduced incidence of root rots. It is important to remove cut materials rather than throwing them back into the bed, particularly in perennial plantings, to avoid providing a source for mildew and *Botrytis* infection.

Weeds. Weeds are best controlled through good pre-plant preparation. Cereal rye cover crops add valuable organic matter to the soil and can provide significant weed suppression by smothering weed seedlings and through allelopathic effects from natural herbicides in the rye. Only a handful of herbicides are currently labeled for flower production. See "Controlling Weeds in Nursery and Landscape Plantings" from The Pennsylvania State University for suggestions (see the references section, page 135). Be sure to read the actual product label carefully. In general, it is easy to find an herbicide to control grasses in flowers, but the choices for broadleaf control are very limited.

The best approach for many growers is the use of plastic mulch for weed control. In vegetable production, some colored plastics have been shown to increase crop yield and decrease pest populations. Results of cut-flower trials at The Pennsylvania State University do not suggest any significant benefit to colored mulches. Weeds must also be controlled between the rows.

Harvest and Postharvest Handling

The plasticulture system for cut-flower production will generally result in harvest seven to 14 days earlier than if black plastic mulch and drip irrigation are not used. The use of clear plastic mulch can result in even earlier harvest but does not provide adequate weed control. White or silver plastic mulch cools the soil and delays harvest but may be useful for late plantings of cool-season crops like snapdragons. Cut flowers from a plasticulture system will generally be cleaner than those from a field production system, which may increase the marketable yield.

Harvesting cut flowers is a very labor-intensive operation. Limit the time required by training and retraining workers. Alan Stevens, author of *Field-Grown Cut Flowers*, suggests several ways to reduce the time required for cut-flower harvesting. He suggests the most effective training reduces the "indecision time"— that is, the time a worker spends trying to reach a decision, in this case about whether a stem should be cut or not. Growers should teach workers what an unacceptable stem looks like. There are fewer of these than acceptable stems, and so decision time is reduced. Workers should also be taught how long to leave the plant stem rather than how long each cut-flower stem should be. This should also reduce decision time, since it eliminates the need to visually assess the length of each stem before deciding where to cut. Cutting should leave behind enough stem for the plant to maintain vigor if recutting is to occur.

Regardless of the production system, flowers should be harvested in the morning after the dew has dried but before the heat of the day. Dead leaves and spent flowers should be removed when the stems are harvested to prevent *Botrytis* (gray mold) from reducing future harvests. Cut flowers need to be placed in water as quickly as possible after cutting and cooled rapidly to reduce water loss and flower aging. Flower stems should be recut under water. A number of devices are available commercially to make this easier.

Many flowers respond well to floral food. Placing the cut stems in a floral food can greatly increase postharvest life. Equally important, clean water and buckets are critical to maximize the postharvest life of cut flowers. The water in buckets of stored flowers should be changed at least daily if floral food is not used, and buckets should be cleaned with a disinfectant between uses. The most common reason for cut flowers to wilt and die prematurely is lack of water caused by bacteria and algae in the water that plug up the cut stems. Any process that reduces the buildup of these microorganisms in the water will improve postharvest longevity. Most floral foods contain antibiotic and acidic agents to reduce microbial growth. Some floral foods also contain ethylene inhibitors. Ethylene can cause premature wilting and petal drop in many flowers.

Cut-flower producers should have a cooler if they want to be able to store cut flowers. Postharvest longevity is directly related to temperature. Most flowers will last longest at cool temperatures (34°–36°F); however, some are chilling-sensitive and should be stored at 40°F or above. Cold storage increases longevity, because it reduces respiration, reduces transpiration, and slows microbial growth. Ethylene in refrigerated storage can greatly reduce the postharvest life of many flowers. Ethylene producers such as apples should not be stored with cut flowers.

The appropriate harvest stage for field-grown cut flowers varies. Some flowers such as yarrows are best harvested as soon as pollen is evident, while sunflowers are best harvested when the flower is almost completely open (table 11-1, page 114).

Plastic Removal and Disposal

Removal and disposal of plastic mulch used in cut-flower plasticulture is the main shortcoming of the system. Plastic must be removed each season, and disposal can be a problem. Although there are machines available to aid in removing plastic mulch, most is removed from the field by hand. One of the major research projects of the Penn State Center for Plasticulture is the development of a system to utilize waste agricultural plastics as a fuel source to address this problem.

Cultivars and Test Results

Many plants are suitable for use as field-grown cut flowers. Primary considerations in selecting cultivars should be flower color and form, postharvest longevity, stem length, ease of production including disease and insect resistance, and potential marketability, not necessarily in that order. Much of the ongoing research in cut-flower plasticulture is devoted to discovering new plants suitable for cut-flower production and the production systems necessary to grow them. Small specialty producers have two things to offer the market: improved quality (their flowers are at least 48 hours fresher than imported flowers) and new and unique items. Producers should trial new cultivars before incorporating them into their production systems. Producers should also visit public gardens and commercial trial sites (like the horticulture trial garden at The Pennsylvania State University) to see new cultivars. The Association of Specialty Cut Flower Growers also sponsors a national evaluation of new cultivars each year.

Marketing

Most flowers are sold as bunches of ten, although some large flowers like sunflowers or expensive items like orchids may be sold individually. Direct-market growers need to provide the freshest, highest-quality product possible to distinguish themselves in a positive way from sellers of low-cost imported flowers. The primary advantage for the local grower is the 48 hours that are required to ship product in from overseas. Poor marketing often limits profitability of local producers.

Flowers are sold through a variety of outlets (table 11-2, page 115). Six basic marketing alternatives are available to most cut-flower growers: wholesale, florists, pick-your-own, roadside stands, farm markets, and subscription sales. In some areas, flower grower cooperatives or auctions may be available for wholesale distribution. Because freshness is always a consideration, growers should always seek to streamline the process from farm to final consumer.

Wholesale

Wholesale distributors generally buy and resell flowers for a predetermined price. These prices are available on the U.S. Department of Agriculture's web site (WWW.USDA.GOV) from specific market terminals. It is important to note that prices vary widely from region to region. This marketing alternative is subject to large price fluctuations, as product rapidly moves in and out of the wholesale marketplace.

TABLE 11-1
Common cut flowers for field plasticulture production

CUT FLOWER	LATIN NAME	HARVEST STAGE	VASE LIFE (days)	COMMENTS
Annual aster	*Callistephus chinensis*	75% flowers open	7–10	Use ethylene inhibitor.
Astilbe	*Astilbe* hybrids	50–75% flowers open	5–8	Use ethylene inhibitor. Place stems in 130°F water, cool to room temperature, and place in floral food.
Bee balm	*Monarda*	25% of blooms 50% open	5–7	Remove bottom leaves. Condition overnight in warm water.
Butterfly weed	*Asclepias tuberosa*	½–⅔ flowers open	5–8	Use ethylene inhibitor. Plunge in cold water. Flowers don't open well after cutting.
Celosia	*Celosia argentea*	Flowers fully developed	7+	Crested types last longer than plumose types.
Columbine	*Aquilegia* hybrids	50% flowers open	5	Use ethylene inhibitor. Place stems in cool water (45°–50°F).
Coneflower	*Rudbeckia*	Open, but centers tight	7–10	Remove foliage. Condition overnight in warm water.
Cosmos	*Cosmos bipinnatus*	Petals just opened	5	Use floral food.
Dahlia	*Dahlia*	Immediately after fully open	7	Use floral food. Remove lower leaves.
Delphinium	*Delphinium* hybrids	½–⅔ flowers open	6–8	Use ethylene inhibitor. Condition overnight in cold water.
Globe amaranth	*Gomphrena globosa*	75% fully opened	7	Condition overnight in water.
Lavender	*Lavendula*	50% flowers open for fresh, 75% open for dried		Condition overnight in warm water.
Lisianthus	*Eustoma grandiflorum*	1 flower fully colored	10–15	Use floral food. Store in light to reduce fading. Sucrose (4–10%) lengthens vase life.
Giant onion	*Allium giganteum*	30% flowers open	14	Use floral food.
False indigo	*Baptesia australis*	⅓ of flowers open	7	Condition overnight in cold water.
Pincushion flower	*Scabiosa caucasica*	50% flowers open	8–12	Use ethylene inhibitor. Condition overnight in cold water up to the flower heads.
Purple coneflower	*Echinacea purpurea*	When petals are expanding	7–10	Use ethylene inhibitor.
Salvia	*Salvia leucantha*	3–4 basal flowers open	7	Use ethylene inhibitor. Always keep in water. Condition overnight in warm water.
Sea holly	*Eryngium* species	Fully open flowers	10–12	Store at 40°F to intensify color.
Snapdragon	*Antirrhinum majus*	50% flowers open	7–10	Use ethylene inhibitor. Condition overnight in warm water (80°–100°F).
Statice	*Limonium sinuatum*	70% flowers open	10–14	Condition in cold water.
Stock	*Matthiola incana*	25–50% flowers open	7–10	Use ethylene inhibitor. Condition in very cold water.
Summer phlox	*Phlox paniculata*	50% flowers open	5–7	Use floral food. Condition overnight in cold water.
Sunflower	*Helianthus annuus*	Almost completely open	7–10	Strip off foliage.
Yarrow	*Achillea filipendula*	Fully open	7–12	
Zinnia	*Zinnia elegans*	Flowers fully open	7–10	Plunge in cold water, condition overnight.

TABLE 11-2
Distribution of fresh-cut flowers

Florist	65.4%
Supermarket	17.7%
Telephone	5.4%
Street vendor	2.0%
Garden center	1.6%
Chain store	1.4%
Convenience store	0.8%
Department store	0.7%
Mail-order catalog	0.4%
Drug store	0.1%
Warehouse/price club	0.0%

SOURCE: *Cut Flower Quarterly,* 1999, 11(3):15

Florists

Market surveys have indicated that nearly 100% of the florists surveyed show at least some willingness to purchase locally grown cut flowers. The high quality and wide selection available through a florist's regular market channels means that their expectations for service and quality from local producers are very high.

Pick-Your-Own, Roadside Stands, and Farm Markets

These sales outlets have the potential to provide substantially higher prices per unit, but may have increased costs for advertising, facility construction, and maintenance.

Subscription Sales

This is an offshoot of the CSA (community-supported agriculture) movement. Most CSAs are based on produce sales, with each member purchasing a share of a farm's production. This is a contract between the grower and each member, which provides for a weekly portion of fruit and vegetables based on production. If a crop is lost, everybody loses; if there is a bumper crop, everybody wins. Some CSAs provide flower shares as part of the contract or as an option.

Cooperatives

Groups of smaller growers pool their product so as to attract larger buyers or explore markets not readily accessible to small producers. A cooperative offers many of the advantages of wholesale marketing while still retaining some local control of product pricing and distribution.

CHAPTER 12

Managing Used Agricultural Plastics

James W. Garthe

After plastic products have served their useful life in agriculture, wouldn't it be nice if they would just disappear? Science tells us that this is impossible—matter can neither be created nor destroyed, so nothing truly disappears. It just gets smaller and smaller until we can no longer see it. Today, farmers can help determine an environmentally sound destiny for their used agricultural plastics.

This chapter will describe some of the technical aspects of plastic as a material and how discarded items are traditionally managed. Despite the limitations of disposal, there are opportunities to pursue.

The Material Called Plastic

Easily identifying types of plastics is the major barrier to managing them. If you do not know what they are, then it is difficult to know their value in the marketplace. If you are able to recognize what is marketable and what is not, then you will be better informed regarding which path your used plastics should follow.

Table 12-1 shows the SPI (Society of the Plastics Industry, Inc.) codes for the more commonly recycled household plastic types called resins. Although the SPI coding system is not perfect, it provides a standard system of identification. Soon this coding will be updated to include newer resins coming into the marketplace.

Plastic can be formed into many shapes, only a few of which will be referred to herein:

- Film—Thin-gauge, flexible material 10 mils or less thick made from a number of different resins. A mil is defined as 1/1000 inch.
- Sheet—Thicker gauge than film; can be bent but not crumpled in the hand.
- Rigid—Molded pieces that cannot be easily bent and retain their shape indefinitely.

A Glimpse at Solid Waste Management

Various options exist to either recover value from used agricultural plastics or dispose of them. Each option has to be managed properly within the community. The energy and resources that are consumed vary with the management option chosen. Currently, many of these practices are neither socially nor environmentally acceptable. A general understanding of waste management will help growers weigh the options.

The U.S. Environmental Protection Agency developed a hierarchy of solid waste management that is based on energy consumption, resource value, environmental damage, and other factors. The hierarchy, depicted in figure 12-1, is the foundation of understanding "the big picture."

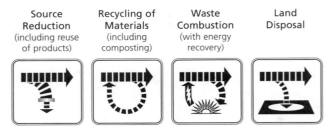

| Source Reduction (including reuse of products) | Recycling of Materials (including composting) | Waste Combustion (with energy recovery) | Land Disposal |

Figure 12-1. Hierarchy of solid waste management in descending order of importance.

Figure 12-2 lists the results of a recent survey of Pennsylvania vegetable growers, revealing what farmers typically do with their plastic wastes. Although data listed is for Pennsylvania, the on-farm waste handling practices are similar across North America.

Concerns

Some concerns are arising in North America of which farmers should be aware. Future legislation could pos-

- ➡ 66% burn on the farm
- ➡ 27% landfill
- ➡ 24% use degradable plastics
- ➡ 20% contract a local waste hauler
- ➡ 13% bury on the farm
- ➡ 12% pile or dump on the farm

Figure 12-2. Agricultural plastic disposal in Pennsylvania. NOTE: Some farms use multiple options.

sibly ban on-farm disposal—including open burning, which is defined as a fire without a flue. Additionally, current burning and dumping practices are leading to a negative public perception of agriculture. Superfund laws do apply to agriculture as a commercial property, so many solid waste management practices of the past are now liabilities that must be dealt with

TABLE 12-1

The Society of the Plastics Industry, Inc., plastic resin code numbering system

SPI PLASTIC CATEGORY	AGRICULTURAL PRODUCTS	CONSUMER PRODUCTS	PRODUCTS MADE FROM RECYCLED PLASTIC	MARKET SHARE (%)
PETE (1 PETE)	Fruit display clamshells	Bottles (soft drink, salad dressing, liquor, and other clear bottles with nubs; mouthwash); jars (peanut butter jars and pickle jars); ovensafe food trays	Soft drink bottles, household cleanser bottles, carpet, paint brushes, scouring pads, surfboards, liquid soap bottles, insulation for clothing	20–30
HDPE (2 HDPE)	Buckets, drums, nursery pots, pesticide containers	Jugs (milk, water, juice, fabric softener); bottles (liquid detergent, bleach, motor oil, antifreeze); butter tubs; grocery bags; toys	Soft drink bottle base cups, detergent and bleach bottles, trash bags, trash cans, recycling bins, traffic barrier cones, plastic lumber, pails, fly swatters	50–60
V (3 V)	PVC pipes, woven irrigation tubing, vinyl siding	Bottles (imported mineral water, floor polish, mouthwash, shampoo, cooking oil, cosmetic liquor); clear food packaging; blister packs	Floor mats, pipes, hoses, mud flaps	5–10
LDPE (4 LDPE)	Sprayer tanks, black PE water tubing, drip tape, mulch film, greenhouse film, hoop house film, silage bags and wraps, disposable boots and gloves, tarps	Food packaging, food wraps, food bags, dry-cleaning bags, dairy product container lids, flexible lids, diaper backing	Garbage can liners, grocery bags, litter bags, convention bags, flying disks, plastic lumber, lawn furniture	5–10
PP (5 PP)	Baling twine, row covers, nursery pots, nursery trays and flats	Bread wrappers, cheese wraps, snack food wraps, cereal box liners, yogurt cups and lids, medicine bottles, bottle labels and caps, rope and straps, combs	Brooms, snow brushes, paint buckets, videocassette storage cases, fast-food trays, lawn mower wheels, auto battery cases, ice scrapers	5–10
PS (6 PS)	Egg cartons, nursery pots, nursery trays and flats, tray inserts	Videocassette cases, compact disc jackets, fast-food clamshell carryouts, hot drink cups, yogurt cups and tubs, disposable cutlery, dairy product containers, cookie and muffin trays	Videocassettes, trash cans, food service trays, building insulation, clipboards, rulers	5–10
Other plastics (7 OTHER)	Syringes, waterproof gloves	Includes all other plastics not mentioned above, multilayered packaging, cookware, lamp housings, name plates, automotive trim, bathtubs, computer housings	Pens, ice scrapers, snow-brushes, street signs	5–10

by the farmer. All this combined may force farmers to conform to the existing solid waste management schemes within their communities. This loss of independence will result in farmers having to reach deeper into their wallets to pay for solid waste management services.

What Are the Options?

Reduce the Use of Plastics

From an environmental standpoint, this is the best option. There are ways to reduce the amount of wastes you generate. To go this route, however, you must decide if you are willing to sacrifice the convenience you have experienced with plasticulture.

Within the reduction concept, there are two approaches that may be palatable. The first is to consider purchasing thinner film plastics, such as mulches. These materials are extraordinarily tough and resilient, yet are less than a mil thick. Less plastic mass means less material to manage later.

A second option is to consider using degradable plastics. Weather conditions affect the rate of their degradation, so many farmers have stopped using the products altogether. You may have to try several brands to get the right formulation for your climate, but the attributes can outweigh the drawbacks, especially from a waste management standpoint.

Reuse the Product Elsewhere

There are several approaches to getting a second life out of plastics. Some ideas may take a bit of creativity on your part. For example, plastic greenhouse films have been cut into manageable sizes and used to cover woodpiles, put by the mailbox with a sign for anyone to pick up, or used as vapor barriers under concrete floors. Certain rigid plastics may be donated to small operations or returned to the supplier for reuse.

Reusing agricultural plastics in plastic lumber makes good sense. The major limitation is that agricultural plastics have a reputation of containing pesticide residues. Although much has been done to help farmers minimize spray drift and overshoot when working with plastics, a change will not happen overnight. A 1998 study at The Pennsylvania State University showed that plastic mulches contain the most amount of pesticide residues and the most amount of dirt and debris. Consequently, marketing attention has shifted toward significantly cleaner greenhouse and dairy films for making quality plastic lumber. The challenge for farmers is to keep plastics as free of pesticides as possible, then develop a working relationship with a manufacturer built upon trust that the plastic source is known and pesticide contamination is controlled or eliminated.

Recycle

Recycling is taking a discarded product and processing it to make it into another product. Figure 12-3 shows the level of processing that is required to recycle film plastic in an industrial operation. Recyclers are picky as to what materials they will purchase, so you should do your part to treat your plastic not as a waste but as a byproduct of farming that may have some economic value.

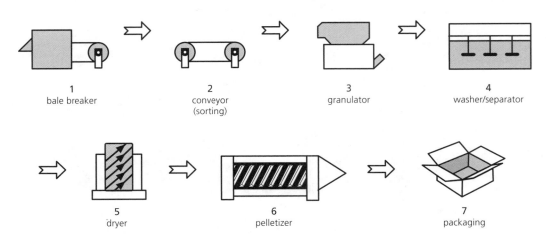

Figure 12-3. Typical processing required for recycling film plastic.

1 bale breaker

2 conveyor (sorting)

3 granulator

4 washer/separator

5 dryer

6 pelletizer

7 packaging

Below are some basic tips to help you market your plastics for recycling.

Know your plastics and keep them separate. Most plastics don't mix when they're melted during recycling. Mixed types are worthless to a buyer and will be rejected. If you don't know the type of plastic that you have, ask your supplier. Keep good records on what plastic type is used at which location on your farm.

Densify. The single most difficult problem is finding a way to compress, or densify, bulky plastic to fill a semitrailer for shipment. The industry wants the material in baled form. Bale sizes vary, but they are typically 800–1,200 pounds, ranging in size from 4 feet x 4 feet x 3 feet to 3 feet x 4 feet x 6 feet. Warning! Using agricultural balers for this purpose can be dangerous, and the bales may be unacceptable for marketing purposes. You may wish to contact your local recycling coordinator to use their baling unit. Some growers use round hay balers for making plastic bales; however, these may not be welcomed by recyclers.

Keep all plastics clean...very clean! Storing plastics is different than storing items that can tolerate some dirt, such as hay, silage, or machinery. You have to "clean up your act" if you want to market your plastic wastes. Ensuring a clean product will put money in your pocket when that product is recycled. If recycling is not feasible, you still benefit from cleanliness, since there's no sense in paying to discard soil, water, or crop residues along with the plastic. Remember:

- No dust, moisture, mud, sod, or soil; store plastic under cover
- No trash, such as weeds, organic matter, rags, or tape
- No loose paper, labels, corrugated cardboard, or paperboard inside bales
- No wood or broken pallet pieces
- No incompatible resins, such as polystyrene (Styrofoam), polyurethane foam (foam rubber), items with paint on them, multilayered items, or multimaterial items
- No strappings, staples, closures, or ties
- No food
- No oil, grease, or paint

STEPS TO PREPARE GREENHOUSE FILM FOR RECYCLING

Step 1. Keep the film clean during stripping.

Step 2. Keep mud and ground water off the film by using film from the first hoop house as a ground cloth. Cut the film on the first house along the nailer or polylock, pulling it across the still-nailed or locked side. Stretch it out in the row or road next to the hoop house, inside surface facing up. If the road is too narrow, cut the film to fit making two or more ground cloths. Next cut the film at the second nailer. The ground cloth is now ready.

Step 3. Do not walk on the ground cloth. This is critical for keeping the film clean.

Step 4. Cut the film on the second hoop house at the nailer alongside the road. It's important to make this cut before moving the ground cloth to prevent anyone from walking on it.

Step 5. Put the ground cloth alongside the second hoop house. Cut the film at the nailer on the side opposite the ground cloth and pull it across the hoops onto the ground cloth. Roll or gather the film from the edge of the cloth.

Step 6. Follow these procedures for remaining hoop houses.

Step 7. If you must tie the bundle of film to move it to the baler, use polyethylene twine only.

Develop a market. Recycling is market-driven, and recyclers will change their addresses or policies routinely. Call them to determine their current terms for accepting deliveries. Some pay shipping costs, some pay for the plastic itself, and some may not pay at all. Send a sample to get their attention and commitment.

The limitations to market development at the current time are:

- It is difficult to identify resins.
- It is expensive to collect and transport bulky, lightweight plastics.
- Contamination leads to problems with quality control, concern over pesticides, and the liability associated with these factors.

- The supply of used materials fluctuates.
- Virgin resins are quite cheap.

To develop a market, consider these ideas:

- Encourage your community or cooperative to purchase a stationary industrial baler.
- Hire custom operators to bale your plastics.
- Write to your plastic supplier, encouraging them to create buy-back, retrieval, or rebate programs.
- Work with your department of agriculture to develop statewide initiatives.

Lastly, the most important thing to remember regarding market development is to **BUY RECYCLED**. That means you have to look at the product labels or specifications page to ensure the products you purchase are made from recycled materials. If you cannot locate this information, urge your supplier to provide a product that is made from recycled materials; consider avoiding those that do not.

Combustion

Combusting, or burning, of wastes can be accomplished in two ways. First, to merely dispose of the plastic, it can be open-burned on the ground or in a container without a flue, leaving only ash for you to deal with. For environmental and health reasons, this approach is not recommended. In contrast, burning can also be a means to capture a large amount of heat energy for useful purposes while managing emissions and ash in desirable ways. There are many words used to clarify this type of burning, such as energy recovery, waste-to-energy, resource recovery, incineration, controlled combustion, and even controlled burning. Whatever the term, the technologies for capturing the heat from burning plastic often cost several million dollars—way beyond the grasp of farmers. Table 12-2 lists the energy values of various materials, including plastic.

Landfilling

This should be your last resort. Landfilling is deemed by society to be "proper disposal," so when all other approaches have been tried, you may have to consider this as a management option. Many sectors of society feel the farmer should be mandated to conform to the

---

ON-FARM BURNING OF PLASTICS

Dirt and debris and the lack of recycling markets in place today may compel you to dispose of your plastics by open burning. Open burning of plastic wastes is illegal in some communities and, if not illegal, it certainly should be discouraged. If you feel you must open burn, then at least burn correctly so you minimize pollution and maximize safety. You can ensure that your fire is as clean as possible by:

- Burning the plastic at a higher temperature. Add sticks or scrap lumber to promote combustion. Smoldering fires have flame temperatures that are 400°–600°F or less, which releases many products of incomplete combustion—or, simply put, air pollution. In contrast, highly efficient combustion units attain 1,800°–2,200°F temperatures and over 99.9% complete combustion, with far less pollutants.
- Making sure the fire gets plenty of air. If you're using a barrel, make sure there are plenty of air holes. A burner with a grate for good aeration is better than a barrel.
- Do not let the pile smolder for hours or days. Pollution increases when a fire smolders.

TABLE 12-2
Heat of combustion of various materials, in British thermal units per pound

WASTE MATERIAL	BTU/POUND
Fuel oil	20,900
Polyethylene plastic	19,900
Polypropylene plastic	19,850
Polystyrene plastic	17,800
Wyoming coal	9,600
Newspaper	8,000
Textiles	6,900
Wood	6,700
Yard wastes	3,000
Food waste	2,600
Average for municipal solid waste	4,500

Source: Adapted from "The Solid Waste Management Problem, No Single Cause, No Single Solution." Published by the Council for Solid Waste Solutions.

waste management plan instituted by the farmer's community, which more often than not entails landfilling.

Future Prospects

Research is continually searching for better solutions to the plastics disposal problem. Several efforts are focusing on ways to recover energy from plastic wastes.

The Pennsylvania State University has developed a process to densify dirty plastics into fuel nuggets called Plastofuel. The steps involved in recycling plasticulture components into these nuggets are illustrated in photos 12-1 through 12-5. The nuggets are designed to be cofired 5–10% with coal in existing boilers. The end-use can be for agricultural boilers or for small community boilers designed to burn coal. The nuggets can be made either on the farm or in small industrial settings,

Photo 12-3. The third step in the making of Plastofuel is taking the roll of retrieved plastic mulch and drip irrigation tape to be densified.

Photo 12-1. Lifting the plastic mulch and drip irrigation tape is the first step in recovery of the energy locked inside it.

Photo 12-4. The fourth step is to make Plastofuel by forcing rigid or film plastic items through a heated die. The die melts the outer layer to encapsulate dirt, debris, and small pieces within the nugget. Shown is mulch film being hand-fed into the prototype machine.

Photo 12-2. The second step is retrieving the plastic mulch and drip irrigation tape.

Photo 12-5. Close-up of the Plastofuel, which can be burned with coal or independently in a burner unit being researched at The Pennsylvania State University.

so the energy is consumed close to the source. The benefit of the system is that it converts an annoying waste into a valuable fuel, with a minimum of energy expended in the process.

Beginning in 2005, the Penn State team will scale up the prototype Plastofuel nugget process to produce 500 pounds per hour. This system will be instrumented to measure energy expenditures, which will better define the economics of the process compared with competing fuels.

Besides heating greenhouses, another possible use for waste plastics is plastic-derived fuel (PDF) for supplemental heating of cement kilns. For the past several years, tire-derived fuel has been used in the production of cement, but now some companies are investigating the use of PDF to reduce their dependency on coal. Lafarge North America is currently working with the Pennsylvania Department of Environmental Protection and a local recycling center to use PDF made from rejected and unmarketable plastic bottles. In time, agricultural plastics might be used in the PDF mix, which will serve as a way to recover energy from a former liability.

New Korean High-Temperature Combustion Technology

Although blending used plastic with coal continues to be an important way to recover energy from waste plastic, a new Korean technology is being investigated by researchers at Penn State. Manufactured by GR Technologies Company, Ltd., this hot-water boiler heating system burns pea-sized pellets made from waste plastics (photo 12-6). The system preheats a series of combustion chambers to 1,650°–2,000°F for 10–15 minutes using fuel oil or kerosene, then automatically switches to the plastic pellets. Field testing of a 396,850-Btu/hour unit for heating high tunnels began at Penn State's Horticulture Research Farm in 2004 (photo 12-7). Eventually, the pellet-fueled unit will be modified to burn the larger and more energy-efficient Plastofuel nuggets, which will be made from agricultural plastics mixed with waste household food and beverage containers.

Testing by the Korea Test Laboratory showed the sys-

tem meets U.S. Environmental Protection Agency (EPA) emissions standards. To verify test results in a field setting, in 2005, researchers will investigate combustion characteristics and efficiencies, air emissions, and overall system heat transfer using a wide array of waste plastic fuels. The projected selling price for the system is $12,000. For more information, contact the author of this chapter (see the references section, page 143).

Photo 12-6. The 396,850-Btu/hour boiler is fueled with pellets made from waste plastic. Hot water heated by the unit is used to heat high tunnels nearby. Here, the burner (right) has been pulled out of the boiler (left) for demonstration purposes to show the flame while burning plastic fuel.

Photo 12-7. Korean boiler technology is being used to heat this high tunnel (background) and soon will be plumbed to heat other tunnels and greenhouses. The burner has been removed from the boiler (right, foreground) to demonstrate the flame while burning pellets made from waste mulch film.

Plasticulture Equipment and Material Sources

Note: The following information was checked for accuracy, but due to the dynamic nature of the Internet, some of the Web site addresses below may no longer be active.

Drip Tape

Chapin Watermatics, Inc.
740 Water Street
PO Box 490
Watertown, NY 13601
Phone: (315) 782-1170
Fax: (315) 782-1490
E-mail: LMITCHELL@CHAPINDRIP.COM
Web site: WWW.CHAPINDRIP.COM

Netafim Irrigation, Inc.
5470 East Home Avenue
Fresno, CA 93727
Phone: (559) 453-6800
Fax: (559) 453-6803
E-mail: NETAFIM@NETAFIMUSA.COM
Web site: WWW.NETAFIM-USA.COM
(drip tubing)

Queen Gil International
POB. 26025
Jerusalem 91260 Israel
Fax: (972) 2-6410313

Rain Bird Agri-Products Co.
633 West Foothill Boulevard
Glendora, CA 91741-2469
Phone: (800) 435-5624
Fax: (626) 852-7310
E-mail: SPRUSIA@RAINBIRD.COM
Web site: WWW.RAINBIRD.COM

Roberts Irrigation Products, Inc.
700 Rancheros Drive

San Marcos, CA 92069-3007
Phone: (760) 744-4511 or (800) 685-5557
Fax: (760) 744-0914
E-mail: CUST-SERV@ROBERTSIRRIGATION.COM
Web site: WWW.ROBERTSIRRIGATION.COM

Toro Agricultural Irrigation
1588 North Marshall Avenue
El Cajon, CA 92020
Phone: (619) 562-2950
Fax: (619) 258-9973
Customer service: (800) 333-8125
Web site: WWW.TOROAG.COM

Trickl-Eez Company
4266 Hollywood Road
St. Joseph, MI 49085
Phone: (616) 429-8200
Fax: (616) 429-6669
E-mail: TRICKLE1@PARRETT.NET
Web site: WWW.TRICKL-EEZ.COM

T-Systems International, Inc.
7545 Carroll Road
San Diego, CA 92121-2401
Phone: (858) 578-1860 or (800) 765-1860
Fax: (858) 578-2344
E-mail: TSYSMKTG@PACBELL.NET
Web site: WWW.TSYSTEMSINTERNATIONAL.COM

Fertilizer Injectors

Agroponic Industries Ltd.
908 Ranchview Cres. NW
Calgary, Alberta, Canada T3G 1P9
Phone: (403) 241-8234
Fax: (403) 241-82138
E-mail: AGROPON@AGROPONIC.COM
Web site: WWW.AGROPONIC.COM

Amiad Filtration Systems Ltd.
2220 Celsius Avenue, Unit B
Oxnard, CA 93030
Phone: (800) 969-4055 or (805) 988-3323
Fax: (805) 988-3313
E-mail: INFO@AMIADUSA.COM
Web site: WWW.AMIADUSA.COM

Dosatron—North and Central America
2090 Sunnydale Boulevard
Clearwater, FL 33765
Phone: (800) 523-8499
E-mail: MAIL@DOSATRONUSA.COM
Web site: WWW.DOSATRONUSA.COM

Dosmatic USA, Inc.
1230 Crowley Circle
Carrollton, TX 75006
Phone: (800)-344-6767 or (972)-245-9765
Fax: 972-245-9000
E-mail: INFO@DOSMATIC.COM
Web site: WWW.DOSMATIC.COM

Mazzei Injector Corporation
500 Rooster Drive
Bakersfield, CA 93307-9555
Phone: (661) 363-6500
Fax: (661) 363-7500
E-mail: MAZZEI@LIGHTSPEED.NET
Web site: WWW.MAZZEI.NET

Equipment

BDI Machinery Sales Co.
430 East Main Street
Macungie, PA 18062-1713
Phone: (800) 808-0454
Fax: (610) 965-2959
E-mail: BDI@JUNO.COM

Buckeye Tractor and Implement, Inc.
5565 State Route 37 East
Delaware, OH 43015
Phone: (740) 363-1341
Fax: (740) 363-6968
E-mail: BT@BUCKEYETRACTOR.COM
Web site: WWW.BUCKEYETRACTOR.COM

Delhi Foundry and Farm Machinery, Ltd.
171 King Street West

Delhi, Ontario, Canada N4B 1X9
Phone: (519) 582-2770
Fax: (519) 582-4442
E-mail: DELHIFOUNDRY@ON.AIBN.COM
Web site: WWW.DELHIFOUNDRY.COM

Ferris Farm Equipment
83 Ferris Road
New Wilmington, PA 16142-9802
Phone: (724) 946-2973
E-mail: FERRISFARM@ADELPHIA.NET
Web site: WWW.FERRISFARM.HOMESTEAD.COM
(Polyplanter)

Holland Transplanter Company
510 East 16th Street
PO Box 1527
Holland, MI 49422-1527
Phone: (616) 392-3579 or (800) 275-4482
Fax: (616) 392-7996
E-mail: HLDTRANS@ISERV.NET
Web site: WWW.TRANSPLANTER.COM

Kennco Manufacturing, Inc.
PO Box 1149
Ruskin, FL 33570
Phone: (813) 645-2591 or (800) 645-2591
Fax: (813) 645-7801
E-mail: KENNCOMFG@AOL.COM
Web site: WWW.KENNCOMFG.COM

Mechanical Transplanter Company
1150 Central Avenue
Holland, MI 49423
Phone: (800) 757-5268
Fax: (616) 396-3619
E-mail: MTC@MECHANICALTRANSPLANTER.COM
Web site: WWW.MECHANICALTRANSPLANTER.COM

Nolts Produce
152 North Hershey Avenue
Leola, PA 17540
Phone: (717) 656-9764

Rain-Flo Irrigation, LLC
884 Center Church Road
East Earl, PA 17519
Phone: (717) 445-6976
Fax: (717) 445-8304
(water-wheel transplanter)

Reddick Fumigants, Inc.
PO Box 391
3002 West Main Street
Williamston, NC 27892
Phone: (252) 792-1613
Fax: (252) 792-4615
Web site: www.reddickfumigants.com

Renaldo Sales and Service, Inc.
1770 Mile Strip Road
North Collins, NY 14111
Phone: (800) 424-5564 or (716) 337-3760
Fax: (716) 337-2756
Web site: www.renaldosales.com

Triangle M Equipment, Ltd.
309 North Polk Street
PO Box 70
Morocco, IN 47963
Phone: (219) 285-2377
Fax: (219) 285-6115
(seeders)

Williames Hi-Tech International Pty. Ltd.
Wills Street
Warragul, Victoria, Australia 3820
Phone: 61-3-5623-5755
Fax: 61-3-5623-5165
E-mail: inquires@whti.com.au
Web site: www.whti.com.au

Row Covers

Agribon+™ PGI Nonwovens
(See web site for distributors.)
Web site: www.agribon.com

American Agrifabrics, Inc.
1282 Old Alpharetta Road
Alpharetta, GA 30005-3986
Phone: (800) 565-5151 or (770) 663-7600
Fax: (770) 663-7690
E-mail: dan@agrifabrics.com

Suntex CP, Inc.
PO Box 21633
Sarasota, FL 34276
Phone: (888) SUNTEX1 or (941) 706-0008
Fax: (941) 942-2998
E-mail: info@suntexcp.com
Web site: www.suntexcp.com

Plastic Mulch

AT Plastics, Inc.
Web site: www.atplas.com

Clarke Ag Plastics
PO Box 238
Greenwood, VA 22943
Phone: (540) 456-4578
Fax: (540) 456-6403
E-mail: agmulch@cstone.net
Web site: www.cstone.net/~agmulch/

Climagro Mulch Film
LECO Industries
3235 Sartelon
Saint-Laurent, Québec, Canada H4R 1E9
Phone: (800) 561-8029
Fax: (514) 332-0406
Web site: www.climagro.com

Green-Tek, Inc.
407 North Main Street
Edgerton, WI 53534
Phone: (800) 747-6440 or (608) 884-9454
Fax: (608) 884-9459
E-mail: greentek@green-tek.com
Web site: www.green-tek.com

Hilex Poly
101 East Carolina Avenue
Hartsville, SC 29550
Phone: (800) 377-2692 or (843) 339-6134
Fax: (843) 332-1277

Integrated Packaging Americas, Inc.
10255 Wilson Avenue SW
Suite 615
Byron Center, MI 49315
Phone: (616) 583-0258
Fax: (616) 583-0257
E-mail: kseese@ipstretch.com

Ken-Bar, Inc.
PO Box 504
25 Walkers Brook Drive
Reading, MA 01867-0704
Phone: (781) 944-0003
Fax: (781) 944-1055
E-mail: info@ken-bar.com
Web site: www.ken-bar.com

Mid South Extrusion, Inc.
2015 Jackson Street
Monroe, LA 71201
Phone: (800) 256-7239 or (318) 322-7239
Fax: (318) 325-7524

PlastiTech, Inc.
478 Notre-Dame PO Box 750
Saint-Rémi, Québec, Canada J0L 2L0
Phone: (800) 667-6279
Fax: (450) 454-6638
E-mail: INFO@PLASTITECH.COM
Web site: WWW.PLASTITECH.COM

Pliant Corporation (formerly Huntsman Packaging Corp)
1475 Woodfield Road
Suite 700
Schaumburg, IL 60173
Phone: (847) 969-3300
Fax: (847) 969-3338
Web site: WWW.PLIANTCORP.COM

Reflectek Foils, Inc.
PO Box 310
1075 Brush Hill Lane
Lake Zurich, IL 60047
Phone: (888) 439-6121
E-mail: RepelGro@aol.com

Rochelle Plastic Films, Inc.
West State Route 38
PO Box 606
Rochelle, IL 61068
Phone: (815) 562-7848
Fax: (815) 562-7849

Tyco Plastics (formerly Armin Plastics)
1401 West 94th Street
Minneapolis, MN 55431
Phone: (800) 873-3941
E-mail: TYCOAG@EARTHLINK.NET
Web site: WWW.TYCOPLASTICS.COM

High Tunnel Frames

Farm Tek
1440 Field of Dreams Way
Dyersville, IA 52040
Phone: (800) 327-6835

Greenhouse Supply, Inc.
12 Acme Road, Suite 212
Brewer, ME 04412
Phone: (800) 696-8511
Web site: WWW.AGROTECH.COM
(dome/gothic-shaped structures)

Haygrove Multibay High Tunnel Systems
U.S. Distributor:
Ralph Cramer
Cramers Posie Patch
116 Trail Road North
Elizabethtown, PA 17022
Phone: (877) CRAMERS/272-6377

Ledgewood Farm
RFD 1, Box 375
Moultonboro, NH 03254
Phone: (603) 476-8829
(peaked/arch-shaped high tunnels)

Rimol Greenhouse Systems, Inc.
40 Londonderry Turnpike
Hooksett, NH 03106
Phone: (603) 629-9004
Web: WWW.RIMOL.COM

Other

ITML Horticultural Products, Inc.
75 Plant Farm Boulevard
PO Box 265
Brantford, Ontario, Canada N3T 5M8
Phone: (519) 753-2666
Fax: (519) 753-1618
E-mail: INFO@ITML.COM
Web site: WWW.ITML.COM
(transplant trays)

Landmark Plastic Corporation
1331 Kelly Avenue
PO Box 7695
Akron, OH 44306
Phone: (330) 785-2200
Fax: (330) 785-9200
(transplants, trays, and pots)

Southern Burner Company
PO Box 885
Chickasha, OK 73023
Phone: (405) 224-5000 or (800) 375-5001
Web site: WWW.SOUTHERNBURNER.COM
(unit heater for small high tunnels)

Speedling Corporation
4300 Old U.S. Highway 41 South
PO Box 7220
Sun City, FL 33586-7220
Phone: (813) 645-3221
Fax: (813) 645-8123
E-mail: SPEEDLING@AOL.COM
Web site: WWW.SPEEDLING.COM
(transplant trays and transplanters)

Tenax Corporation
4800 East Monument Street
Baltimore, MD 21205
Phone: (800) 356-8495
Fax: (410) 522-7015
E-mail: INFO@US.TENAX.COM
Web site: WWW.TENAXUS.COM
(support material for cut flowers)

Glossary

Abrasion Injury — Injury observed on plants that was caused by sand, hail, or wind resulting in moderate to severe tissue loss on stems, leaves, flowers, or fruit.

Absorptivity — The property of a body that determines the fraction of incident radiation absorbed by the body.

Anthesis — The opening of flowers with appropriate plant parts available for pollination.

Available Water in Soils — The part of the water in the soil that can be taken up by plants at rates significant to their growth; usable water; obtainable water.

Antioxidant — Formulation ingredient that prevents or slows down oxidation of plastic material exposed to air.

Backflow — A flowing back or return of water to its source (such as a well or pond).

Blackbody — An ideal body or surface that completely absorbs all radiant energy of any wavelength falling upon it with no reflection of energy.

Blown Film — A thermoplastic film that is produced by extruding a tube, applying a slight internal pressure to the tube to expand it while still molten, and subsequently cooling the tube to set it. The tube is then flattened through guides and wound up flat on rolls. The size of the blown film is determined by the flat width in inches.

Capillary Porosity — The small pores or the bulk volume of small pores that hold water in soils against a tension usually greater than 60 centimeters of water. These pores are commonly filled with water when the soil is at field capacity.

Cation Exchange Capacity — The total quantity of cations that a soil can adsorb by cation exchange, usually expressed as milliequivalents per 100 grams of soil. Measured values of cation exchange capacity depend somewhat on the method used for the determination.

Chemigation — Application of various pesticides through an irrigation system.

Convection — Transfer of energy in fluid motion.

Desiccation — A drying out of plant material or soil.

Double Cropping — Production of two different crops in a given area in the same year.

Easily Available Water — The portion of water in the soil that is readily absorbed by plant roots, usually capillary water between 0.3 and 15 bars of suction.

Elasticity — That property of a material by virtue of which it tends to recover its original size and shape after deformation. The tendency of a material to recover its natural size and shape when deforming load is removed.

Embossing — Techniques used to create depressions of a specific pattern in plastic film and sheeting.

Erosion — The wearing away of the land surface by detachment and transport of soil and rock materials through the action of moving water, wind, or other geological agents.

Evapotranspiration — The total loss of water by evaporation from the soil and by transpiration from plants for a given area.

Fertigation — Application of soluble fertilizers through a drip irrigation system.

Field Capacity — The percentage of water remaining in a soil two or three days after having been saturated and after drainage due to gravity has stopped.

Fumigation — Treatment of soil with a volatile or gaseous fumigate for the control of crop pests (soil pathogens, soil insects, and weeds).

Gas Transmission — The movement of gas through film materials. The gas transmission property (permeability) of a film is measured in terms of volume of gas (at standard temperature and pressure) transmitted through a given area of film of a given thickness within a given time.

Growing Degree Days (GDD) — Method for calculating the amount of heat units based on daily temperatures that contribute to the physiological growth and development of plants.
$$GDD = Temp_{min} + Temp_{max} \div 2 - base\ 40°F\ or\ 50°F$$

Hardpan — A hardened or cemented soil horizon or layer. The soil material may be sandy or clayey and may be cemented by iron oxide, silica, calcium carbonate, or other substances.

High Tunnel — Structure that resembles a plastic-covered greenhouse, has no automated heating or venting, is temporary, and is covered with a single layer of 6-mil plastic.

Integrated Crop Management (ICM) — A management system that recognizes and integrates the individual production practices required for success and profitability as dependent variables that can be controlled by the grower in some cases (such as using drip irrigation to control plant growth or using row covers to modify/prevent frost damage to crops).

Infrared Light — Light that is outside the visible spectrum at its red end (greater than 800 nanometers).

Injectors — Devices that are able to inject (mix) concentrated fertilizers and chemicals with flowing water in an irrigation system. There are two types of injectors: venturi (vacuum type) and hydraulic (in which water drives a piston pump).

Langley — A unit of solar radiation equivalent to one gram calorie per square centimeter of irradiated surface.

Leaching — The removal of materials (elements) in solution by the passage of water through soil.

Light Transmission — The percentage of total available light that passes through a material.

Low Tunnel — A structure placed over crop rows in the field consisting of #9 wire bent in a half circle with a peak height of 18–36 inches from the soil surface. Either plastic film with vent holes or slits or row cover material is placed over the hoops and secured on both sides with soil.

Mil — A unit of length equal to 0.001 inch, often used for reporting film thickness. To convert mil to millimeter, multiply by 0.0254.

Nanometer — A unit of length equal to 1/1000 of a micron. A micron equals 1/1000 of a millimeter.

Opacity — The measure of how opaque or see-through a plastic film is. Certain pigments added to the polyethylene resin will make the plastic more opaque or less see-through.

Oxidation — Removal of electrons from a molecule.

Percolation — The downward movement of water through soil.

Photosynthetic Active Radiation (PAR) — The measured flux between 400 and 700 nanometers that is utilized by plants during the carbohydrate-producing reactions of photosynthesis.

Phytochrome — pigment in plants in small concentrations that exists in two photoreversible forms, the red form and the far-red form.

Plasticulture — The use of plastics in agriculture for both plant and animal production, including plastic mulch, drip irrigation, row covers, low tunnels, high tunnels, greenhouses, silage bags, hay bales, food packaging, and nursery pots and containers for growing transplants.

Polyethylene — Plastic of which there are two major types with different chain structures: (1) stiffer, stronger, linear material sometimes called high-density polyethylene (HDPE) and (2) low-pressure and more flexible, lower melting, branched polyethylene known as low-density (LDPE) or high-pressure polyethylene. More recently, linear low-density polyethylene (LLDPE) has become a major product.

Radiant Flux — A measure of radiometric power. Radiometric flux, expressed in watts, includes light at all wavelengths of the spectrum: ultraviolet (200–400 nanometers), visible (400–700 nanometers), and infrared (700–30,000 nanometers).

Reflectance — Energy that has not been transmitted or absorbed.

Root Zone — The part of the soil that is penetrated or can be penetrated by plant roots.

Row Covers — Flexible, transparent coverings made from polyester or polypropylene that are installed over single or multiple rows of horticultural crops for the purpose of enhancing plant growth by warming the air around the plants in the field.

Runoff — That portion of precipitation on a drainage area that is discharged from the area in stream channels. Types include surface runoff, groundwater runoff, or seepage.

Sandblasting — Damage caused to plants (young plants especially) by blowing sand. Moderate to extreme sandblasting can damage stems and kill plants.

Sand Media Filter — Filters that are steel tanks filled with sharp or coarse sand. The sand bed creates the filtration as water passes through it; silt and algae remain in the sand as the water passes through.

Soil Moisture Tension — The force by which moisture is held in the soil. It is a negative pressure and

may be expressed in any convenient pressure unit. Tension does not include osmotic pressure values.

Solarization — A simple nonchemical technique that captures radiant heat energy from the sun. This energy causes physical, chemical, and biological changes in the soil. These changes lead to control or suppression of soilborne plant pathogens such as fungi, bacteria, nematodes, and pests along with weed seeds and seedlings.

Solar Infrared Energy — That portion of sunlight ranging from 700 to 2,500 nanometers in wavelength, often called "near infrared." "Far infrared" or blackbody radiation ranges from 2,500 to 10,000 nanometers.

Solar Radiation — The entire energy spectrum (all wavelengths) created by the sun. The wavelengths reaching earth range from 300 to 3,000 nanometers.

Solenoid Valve — Water valves that open by electrical impulse and not manually.

Subirrigation — Applying irrigation water below the ground surface either by raising the water table within or near the root zone, or by using a buried perforated or porous pipe system that discharges water directly into the root zone.

Tensiometer — A device having a sealed, water-filled ceramic tip on the lower end and a vacuum gauge on the upper end to measure the amount of water in a soil.

Thermal Radiation — Electromagnetic radiation emitted from a heat or light source as a consequence of its temperature; it consists essentially of ultraviolet, visible, and infrared radiation.

Translocation — The movement of carbohydrates from photosynthesis in the plant from one part of a plant to another.

Transpiration — The evaporative loss of water (as water vapor) from plants, mostly through their stomata.

Triple Cropping — Production of three different crops in a given area in the same year.

Ultraviolet (UV) — Zone of invisible radiation beyond the violet end of the spectrum of visible radiation. Since UV wavelengths are shorter than the visible wavelengths, their photons have more energy, enough to initiate some chemical reactions and to degrade most plastic.

Ultraviolet (UV) Light — That portion of sunlight ranging in wavelength from 200 to 400 nanometers. Wavelengths below 300 nanometers do not pass through the atmosphere in appreciable amounts.

Venturi Injector — A type of injector that operates by generating a differential pressure or vacuum across a venturi device. This action draws a chemical into the drip irrigation system.

Windbreak — A narrow barrier of living trees or combination of trees and shrubs, usually from one to five rows wide, established within or around a field for the protection of land and crops. May also consist of narrow strips of annual crops such as corn, sorghum, or wheat.

Useful Conversions

TYPE OF MEASUREMENT	TO CONVERT:	INTO:	MULTIPLY BY:
Length	centimeters (cm)	inches (in)	0.394
	feet (ft)	centimeters (cm)	30.48
	feet (ft)	inches (in)	12
	feet (ft)	yards (yd)	0.33
	inches (in)	feet (ft)	0.083
	inches (in)	millimeters (mm)	25.4
	inches (in)	centimeters (cm)	2.54
	meters (m)	inches (in)	39.37
	meters (m)	feet (ft)	3.281
	meters (m)	yards (yd)	1.094
	yards (yd)	feet (ft)	3
	yards (yd)	centimeters (cm)	91.44
	yards (yd)	meters (m)	0.9144
Area	acres	square feet (ft^2)	43,560.0
	acres	square yards (yd^2)	4,840.0
	acres	hectares (ha)	0.4047
	hectares (ha)	acres	2.471
	hectares (ha)	square meters (m^2)	10,000.0
	square inches (in^2)	square centimeters (cm^2)	6.452
	square centimeters (cm^2)	square inches (in^2)	0.155
	square feet (ft^2)	square centimeters (cm^2)	929.09
	square feet (ft^2)	square meters (m^2)	0.0929
	square meters (m^2)	square feet (ft^2)	10.76
	square meters (m^2)	square yards (yd^2)	1.196
Weight	grams (g)	ounces (oz)	0.0353
	kilograms (kg)	pounds (lb)	2.205
	metric tons (megagrams)	short tons	1.1023
	ounces (oz)	pounds (lb)	0.0625
	ounces (oz)	grams (g)	28.35
	pounds (lb)	ounces (oz)	16
	pounds (lb)	grams (g)	453.6
	short tons	metric tons (megagrams)	0.9078

TYPE OF MEASUREMENT	TO CONVERT:	INTO:	MULTIPLY BY:
Volume, solids	bushels (bu)	cubic feet (ft³)	1.24
	bushels (bu)	cubic meters (m³)	0.352
	bushels (bu)	liters (L)	35.24
	cubic feet (ft³)	liters (L)	28.32
	cubic feet (ft³)	U.S. gallons (gal)	7.48
	cubic feet (ft³)	cubic inches (in³)	1,728.0
	cubic feet (ft³)	cubic yards (yd³)	0.037
	cubic feet (ft³)	bushels (bu)	0.804
	cubic inches (in³)	milliliters (ml)	16.39
	cubic meters (m³)	cubic yards (yd³)	1.308
	cubic meters (m³)	U.S. gallons (gal)	264.2
	cubic meters (m³)	cubic feet (ft³)	35.3
	cubic yards (yd³)	cubic feet (ft³)	27
	cubic yards (yd³)	liters (L)	764.6
	cubic yards (yd³)	cubic meters (m³)	0.765
	cubic yards (yd³)	bushels (bu)	21.7
	gallons, U.S. dry (gal)	cubic inches (in³)	269.0
	liters (L)	cubic inches (in³)	61.02
	milliliters (mL)	cubic inches (in³)	0.0610
	quarts, dry (qt)	cubic inches (in³)	67.2
Volume, liquids	cubic centimeters (cm³ or cc)	milliliters (mL)	1
	cups (c)	fluid ounces (fl oz)	8
	gallons, U.S. (gal)	cups (c)	16.0
	gallons, U.S. (gal)	cubic inches (in³)	231.0
	gallons, U.S. (gal)	quarts (qt)	4
	gallons, U.S. (gal)	liters (L)	3.785
	gallons, U.S. (gal)	gallons, Imperial (gal)	0.833
	gallons, Imperial (gal)	cubic inches (in³)	277.42
	gallons, Imperial (gal)	liters (L)	4.546
	gallons, Imperial (gal)	gallons, U.S. (gal)	1.20
	liters (L)	pints (pt)	2.113
	liters (L)	quarts (qt)	1.057
	liters (L)	gallons, U.S. (gal)	0.2642
	milliliters (mL)	fluid ounces (fl oz)	0.0338
	pints (pt)	fluid ounces (fl oz)	16.0
	pints (pt)	cups (c)	2
	pints (pt)	quarts (qt)	0.5
	pints (pt)	cubic inches (in³)	28.87
	pints (pt)	liters (L)	0.4732
	fluid ounces (fl oz)	cubic inches (in³)	1.805
	fluid ounces (fl oz)	tablespoons (Tbsp)	2
	fluid ounces (fl oz)	teaspoons (tsp)	6
	fluid ounces (fl oz)	milliliters (mL)	29.57

TYPE OF MEASUREMENT	TO CONVERT:	INTO:	MULTIPLY BY:
Volume, liquids (continued)	quarts (qt)	fluid ounces (fl oz)	32
	quarts (qt)	cups (c)	4
	quarts (qt)	pints (pt)	2
	quarts (qt)	U.S. gallons, liquid (gal)	0.25
	quarts (qt)	cubic inches (in^3)	57.7
	quarts (qt)	liters (L)	0.9463
	tablespoons (Tbsp)	teaspoons (tsp)	3
	tablespoons (Tbsp)	milliliters (mL)	15
	teaspoons (tsp)	milliliters (mL)	5
Weight per volume	grams/cubic centimeter (g/cm^3)	pounds/cubic foot (lbs/ft^3)	62.3
	tablespoons/bushel (Tbsp/bu)	pounds/cubic yard (lbs/yd^3)	1 (approx.)
	pounds/cubic yard (lbs/yd^3)	ounces/cubic foot (oz/ft^3)	0.6
	ounces/cubic foot (oz/ft^3)	pounds/cubic yard (lbs/yd^3)	1.67
	pounds/cubic yard (lbs/yd^3)	grams/liter (g/L)	0.595
	kilograms/cubic meter (kg/m^3)	pounds/cubic yard (lbs/yd^3)	1.6821

Parts per Million (ppm) Conversions
• 1 milligram/liter = 1 ppm
• 1 ounce/gallon = 7,490 ppm
• 1 ounce/100 gallons = 75 ppm

percent fertilizer element x 75 = ppm of element in 100 gallons of water per ounce of fertilizer

For example, for a 9-45-15 fertilizer, the ppm nitrogen (N) in 100 gallons of water per ounce of fertilizer would be:
0.09 (percent N) x 75 = 6.75 ppm N in 100 gallons of water per ounce of 9-45-15

If you want 150 ppm N, and each ounce gives 6.75 ppm, then you need:
150 ÷ 6.75 = 22.22 ounces of 9-45-15 fertilizer in 100 gallons of water

Temperature Conversion Formulas
• To convert °C to °F: (°C x 9/5) + 32 = °F
• To convert °F to °C: (°F – 32) x 5/9 = °C

References

NOTE: Due to the dynamic nature of the Internet, some of the Web site addresses below may no longer be active.

Web Sites on Plasticulture

American Society of Plasticulture:
<HTTP://WWW.PLASTICULTURE.ORG>

Penn State Center for Plasticulture:
<HTTP://PLASTICULTURE.CAS.PSU.EDU>

Chapter 1: Plasticulture—An Introduction

Bogle, O. and T. K. Hartz. 1986. Comparison of drip and furrow irrigation for muskmelon production. *HortScience* 21: 242–244.

Bonanno, R. A., 1996. Weed management in plasticulture. *HortTechnology* 6 (3): 186–189.

Clark, G. A., C. D. Stanley, D. N. Maynard, G. J. Hochmuth, E. A. Hanlon, and D. Z. Haman. 1991. Water and fertilizer management of microirrigated fresh market tomatoes. *Transactions of the American Society of Agricultural Engineers* 34: 429–435.

Dix, M. E. and D. Leatherman. 1988. Insect management in windbreaks. In *Windbreak Technology: Proceedings of an International Symposium on Windbreak Technology*, ed. J. R. Brandle, D. L. Hintz, and J. W. Sturrock, 501–502. New York: Elsevier.

Emmert, E. M. 1957. Black polyethylene for mulching vegetables. *Proceedings of the American Society for Horticultural Science* 69: 464–469.

Hall, B. J. and S. T. Besemer. 1972. Agricultural plastics in California. *HortScience* 7: 373–378.

Hemphill, D. D. 1993. Agricultural plastics as solid waste: What are the options for disposal? *HortTechnology* 3 (1): 70–73.

Hochmuth, G. J. 1992. Fertilizer management for drip irrigated vegetable in Florida. *HortTechnology* 2: 27–32.

Hodges, L., M. E. Dix, J. Brandle, R. Wright, and M. Harrell. 1994. Effects of shelterbelts on insect pests in muskmelon. *Proceedings of the Nebraska Fruit and Vegetable Growers Conference*, 18–19.

Lamont, W. J. and E. B. Poling. 1986. A fresh way of looking for profits: Double-cropping strawberries, muskmelons. *Fruit South* 7 (4): 8–11.

Lamont, W. J., K. A. Sorensen, and C. W. Averre. 1990. Painting aluminum strips on black plastic mulch reduces mosaic symptoms on summer squash. *HortScience* 25: 1305.

Marr, C. W. and W. J. Lamont. 1992. Profits, profits, profits—three good reasons to try triple cropping. *American Vegetable Grower* 40: 18, 20.

Natwick, E. T. and A. Durazo, III. 1985. Polyester covers protect vegetables from whiteflies and virus disease. *California Agriculture* 39 (7 and 8): 21–22.

Scoville, R. H. and D. Leaman. 1965. Polyethylene uses in soil fumigation. Proceedings of the 6th National Agricultural Plastics Conference, 98–99

Stapleton, J. J. 1991. Use of soil solarization for the control of soil pests. *Proceedings of the 23rd National Agricultural Plastics Congress*, 266–271.

Wells, O. S. 1991. High tunnels shelter early crops. *American Vegetable Grower* 39 (2): 44, 46–47.

Wells, O. S. and J. B. Loy. 1985. Intensive vegetable production with rowcovers. *HortScience* 20: 822–826.

Chapter 2: Plastic Mulches

Cebula, S. 1995. Black and transparent plastic mulches in greenhouse production of sweet pepper. II. Light conditions and the generative development of plants. *Folia Horticulturae* 7: 59–67.

Decoteau, D. R., M. J. Kasperbauer, D. D. Daniels, and P. G. Hunt. 1988. Plastic mulch color effects on reflected light and tomato plant growth. *Scientia Horticulturae* 34: 169–175.

Decoteau, D. R., M. J. Kasperbauer, and P. G. Hunt. 1989. Mulch surface color affects yield of fresh-market tomatoes. *Journal of the American Society for Horticultural Science* 114: 216–219.

Ennis, R. S. 1987. Plastigone—a new, time-controlled photodegradable plastic mulch film. *Proceedings of the 20th National Agricultural Plastics Congress,* 83–90.

Graham, H. A., D. R. Decoteau, and D. E. Linvill. 1995. Development of a polyethylene mulch system that changes color in the field. *HortScience* 30: 265–269.

Ham, J. M. and G. J. Kluitenberg. 1994. Modeling the effect of mulch optical properties and mulch-soil contact resistance on soil heating under plastic mulch culture. *Agricultural and Forest Meteorology* 71: 403–424.

Ham, J. M., G. J. Kluitenberg, and W. J. Lamont. 1993. Optical properties of plastic mulches affect the field temperature regime. *Journal of the American Society for Horticultural Science* 228 (2): 188–193.

Hemphill, D. D. 1993. Agricultural plastics as solid waste: What are the options for disposal? *HortTechnology* 3 (1): 70–73.

Lamont, W. J., K. A. Sorensen, and C. W. Averre. 1990. Painting aluminum strips on black plastic mulch reduces mosaic symptoms on summer squash. *HortScience* 25: 1305.

Liakatas, A., J. A. Clark, and J. L. Monteith. 1986. Measurements of the heat balance under plastic mulches. Part I. Radiation balance and soil heat flux. *Agricultural and Forest Meteorology* 36: 227–239.

Loy, B., J. Lindstrom, S. Gordon, D. Rudd, and O. Wells. 1989. Theory and development of wavelength selective mulches. *Proceedings of the 21st National Agricultural Plastics Congress,* 193–197.

Loy, B., O. S. Wells, N. Karakoudas, and K. Milbert. 1998. Comparative effects of red and black polyethylene mulch on growth, assimilate partitioning, and yield in trellised tomato. *Proceedings of the 27th National Agricultural Plastics Congress,* 188–197.

Orzolek, M. D. and J. H. Murphy. 1993. The effect of colored polyethylene mulch on the yield of squash and pepper. *Proceedings of the 24th National Agricultural Plastics Congress,* 157–161.

Schales, F. D. and R. Sheldrake. 1963. Mulch effects on soil conditions and tomato plant response. *Proceedings of the 4th National Agricultural Plastics Conference,* 78–90.

Tanner, C. B. 1974. Microclimate modification: Basic concepts. *HortScience* 9: 555–560.

Chapter 3:
Drip Irrigation and Water Management

Anonymous. *Water Quality and Treatment.* Hach Chemical Company, <WWW.HACH.COM>.

Clark, G. A. and A. G. Smajstrla. 1996. Design considerations for vegetable crop drip irrigation systems. *HortTechnology* 6 (3): 155–159.

Lamont, W. J., Jr. April 1991. Drip irrigation: Part of a complete vegetable production package. *Irrigation Journal.* Cathedral City, CA: Adams/Green Industry Publishing. (4-page reprint)

Ross, D. S. 1997. *Trickle Irrigation for Cut flowers, Vegetables, and Small Fruit.* Bulletin 356. College Park, MD: Maryland Cooperative Extension.

Ross, D. S. November/December 1999. Prevent clogging in drip irrigation lines with chlorine. *Irrigation Journal.* ePublished at <WWW.GREENMEDIAONLINE.COM/IJ/1999/1299/>. Adams Business Media, Inc.

Ross, D. S. and H. L. Brodie. 1984. *Gypsum Blocks for Irrigation Management.* Biological resources engineering FACTS 149. College Park, MD: Department of Biological Resources Engineering, University of Maryland.

Ross, D. S., H. L. Brodie, and L. E. Carr. 1984. *Tensiometers for Irrigation Management.* Biological resources engineering FACTS 146. College Park, MD: Department of Biological Resources Engineering, University of Maryland.

Ross, D. S. and C. A. McClurg. 1990 (revision). *Trickle Irrigation for Vegetable Crops.* Biological resources engineering FACTS 109. College Park, MD: Department of Biological Resources Engineering, University of Maryland.

Storlie, C. A. 1995. *Irrigation Scheduling with Tensiometers.* Fact Sheet 657. New Brunswick, NJ: Rutgers Cooperative Extension, Rutgers—The State University of New Jersey.

Storlie, C. A. 1995. *Treating Drip Irrigation Systems with Chlorine.* Fact sheet 795. New Brunswick, NJ: Rutgers Cooperative Extension, Rutgers—The State University of New Jersey.

T-Systems International, Inc. 1998. *Introduction to Drip Irrigation.* Bulletin TS–22097.

Chapter 4: Fertigation of Vegetable Crops

Clark, G. A. and D. Z. Haman. 1988. *Microirrigation in Mulched-Bed Production Systems: Irrigation Depths.* Agricultural engineering fact sheet AE–72. Gainesville, FL: University of Florida Cooperative Extension.

Clark, G. A., D. N. Maynard, C. D. Stanley, G. J. Hochmuth, E. A. Hanlon, and D. Z. Haman. 1990b. *Irrigation Scheduling and Management of Micro irrigated Tomatoes.* Circular 872. Gainesville, FL: University of Florida Cooperative Extension Service.

Clark, G. A., A. G. Smajstrla, D. Z. Haman, and F. S. Zazueta. 1990a. *Injection of Chemicals into Irrigation Systems: Rates, Volumes, and Injection Periods.* Bulletin 250. Gainesville, FL: University of Florida Cooperative Extension.

Clark, G. A., A. G. Smajstrla, and F. S. Zazueta. 1989. *Atmospheric Parameters which Affect Evaporation.* Circular 822. Gainesville, FL: University of Florida Cooperative Extension Service.

Clark, G. A., C. D. Stanley, D. N. Maynard, D. Z. Haman, G. J. Hochmuth, and E. A. Hanlon. 1988b. Tensiometers as a management tool for micro irrigated tomatoes in southwest Florida. *Proceedings of the Florida Tomato Institute.* University of Florida Cooperative Extension SS 801: 15.

Clark, G. A., C. D. Stanley, and A. G. Smajstrla. 1988a. *Microirrigation on Mulched-Bed Systems: Components, System Capacities, and Management.* Agricultural engineering bulletin 245. Gainesville, FL: University of Florida Cooperative Extension.

Dangler, J. M. and S. J. Locascio. 1990a. Yield of trickle irrigated tomatoes as affected by time of N and K application. *Journal of the American Society for Horticultural Science* 115: 585–589.

Dangler, J. M. and S. J. Locascio. 1990b. External and internal blotchy ripening and fruit elemental content of trickle irrigated tomatoes as affected by N and K application time. *Journal of the American Society for Horticultural Science* 115: 547–549.

Elmstrom, G. W., S. J. Locascio, and J. M. Myers. 1981. Watermelon response to drip and sprinkler irrigation. *Proceedings of the Florida State Horticultural Society* 94: 161–163.

Fiskell, J. G. A. and S. J. Locascio. 1983. Changes in available N for drip-irrigated tomatoes from preplant and fertigation N sources. *Soil and Crop Science Society of Florida Proceedings* 42: 180–184.

Garrison, S. A. et al. 1999. *Commercial Vegetable Production Recommendations.* Extension bulletin E0010. New Brunswick, NJ: Rutgers—The State University of New Jersey.

Graetz, D. A., J. G. A. Fiskell, S. J. Locascio, B. Zur, and J. M. Meyers. 1978. Chloride and bromide movement with trickle irrigation of bell peppers. *Proceedings of the Florida State Horticultural Society* 91: 319–322.

Haman, D. Z., and F. T. Izuno. 1987. *Principles of Microirrigation.* Agricultural engineering misc. report 85–15. Gainesville, FL: University of Florida Cooperative Extension.

Haman, D. Z., A. G. Smajstrla, and F. S. Zazueta. 1986. *Media Filters for Trickle Irrigation in Florida.* Agricultural engineering fact sheet AE–57. Gainesville, FL: University of Florida Cooperative Extension.

Haman, D. Z., A. G. Smajstrla, and F. S. Zazueta. 1988a. *Screen Filters in Trickle Irrigation Systems.* Agricultural engineering fact sheet AE–6 1. Gainesville, FL: University of Florida Cooperative Extension.

Haman, D. Z., A. G. Smajstrla, and F. Zazueta. 1988b. *Water Quality Problems Affecting Microirrigation in Florida.* Agricultural engineering report SS–AGE–805. Gainesville, FL: University of Florida Cooperative Extension.

Hochmuth, G. J. 1990a. Fertilizer management for drip irrigated watermelons. *Proceedings of the Florida Watermelon Institute,* University of Florida Cooperative Extension Special Series SS-VEC-003: 10–18.

Hochmuth, G. J. 1990b. Pepper fertilization recommendations. *Proceedings of the Florida Pepper Institute,* University of Florida Cooperative Extension Special Series SS-VEC-002: 57–65.

Hochmuth, G. J. 1990c. Tomato fertilizer management. *Proceedings of the Florida Tomato Institute,* University of Florida Cooperative Extension Special Series SS-VEC-001:84–94.

Hochmuth, G. J., P. R. Gilreath, E. A. Hanlon, G. A. Clark, D. N. Maynard, C. D. Stanley, and D. Z. Haman. 1988. Evaluating plant N status with plant sap quick-test kits. *Proceedings of the Florida Tomato Institute,* University of Florida Cooperative Extension Special Series SS-VEC-801: 6–14.

Hochmuth, G. J. and E. A. Hanlon. 1989. *Commercial Vegetable Crop Nutrient Requirements.* Circular 806. Gainesville, FL: University of Florida Cooperative Extension.

Hochmuth, G. J. and E. A. Hanlon. Unpublished. Research results with potassium requirements for mulched vegetables in Florida.

Hochmuth, G., E. Hanlon, P. Gilreath, and K. Shuler. 1989. Results of nitrogen and potassium demonstrations for tomatoes in south Florida. *Proceedings of the Florida Tomato Institute,* University of Florida Cooperative Extension Special Series SS-VEC-901: 50–63.

Kidder, G., E. A. Hanlon, and G. J. Hochmuth. 1989. IFAS standardized fertilization recommendations for vegetable crops. *University of Florida Cooperative Extension Notes in Soil Science* No. 38. SS-SOS-907.

Kovach, S. P. 1984. *Determination of Water Requirements for Florida Vegetables.* Circular 607. Gainesville, FL: University of Florida Cooperative Extension.

Locascio, S. J. and J. G. A. Fiskell. 1979. Pepper response to sulfur coated urea, mulch, and nitrogen rate. *Proceedings of the Florida State Horticultural Society* 92: 112–115.

Locascio, S. J., J. G. A. Fiskell, and G. W. Elmstrom. 1978. Comparison of sulfur coated and uncoated urea for watermelons. Soil and Crop Science *Society of Florida Proceedings* 37: 197–200.

Locascio, S. J., J. G. A. Fiskell, and F. G. Martin. 1981a. Responses of bell pepper to nitrogen sources. *Journal of the American Society for Horticultural Science* 106: 628–632.

Locascio, S. J., J. G. A. Fiskell, and F. G. Martin. 1984. Nitrogen sources and combinations for polyethylene mulched tomatoes. *Proceedings of the Florida State Horticultural Society* 97: 148–150.

Locascio, S. J. and F. G. Martin. 1985. Nitrogen source and application timing for trickle-irrigated strawberries. *Journal of the American Society for Horticultural Science* 110: 820–823.

Locascio, S. J., J. M. Myers, and J. G. A. Fiskell. 1982. Nitrogen application timing and source for drip irrigated tomatoes. In *Ninth International Plant Nutrition Colloquium,* ed. A. Scaife, 323–328. England: Warwick University.

Locascio, S. J., J. M. Myers, and S. R. Kostewicz. 1981b. Quantity and rate of water application for drip irrigated tomatoes. *Proceedings of the Florida State Horticultural Society* 91: 163–166.

Locascio, S. J., S. M. Olson, and F. M. Rhoads. 1989. Water quantity and time of N and K application for trickle-irrigated tomatoes. *Journal of the American Society for Horticultural Science* 114: 265–268.

Locascio, S. J., S. M. Olson, F. M. Rhoads, C. D. Stanley, and A. A. Csizinszky. 1985. Water and fertilizer timing for trickle-irrigated tomatoes. *Proceedings of the Florida State Horticultural Society* 98: 237–239.

Locascio, S. J. and A. G. Smajstrla. 1989. Drip-irrigated tomato as affected by water quantity and N and K application timing. *Proceedings of the Florida State Horticultural Society* 102: 307–309.

Mikkelsen, R. L. 1989. Phosphorus fertilization through drip irrigation. *Journal of Production Agriculture* 2: 279–286.

Persaud, N., S. J. Locascio, and C. M. Geraldson. 1976. Effect of rate and placement of nitrogen and potassium on yield of mulched tomato using different irrigation methods. *Proceedings of the Florida State Horticultural Society* 89: 135–138.

Persaud, N., S. J. Locascio, and C. M. Geraldson. 1977. Influence of fertilizer rate and placement and irrigation method on plant nutrient status, soil soluble salt and root distribution of mulched tomatoes. *Soil and Crop Science Society of Florida Proceedings* 36: 122–125.

Rhoads, F. M. 1990. *Irrigation Use by Mulched Staked Tomatoes in North Florida.* Quincy research report 90–17. Gainesville, FL: University of Florida Agricultural Experiment Station NFREC.

Rolston, D. E., R. S. Rauschkolb, C. J. Phene, R. J. Miller, K. Urier, R. M. Carlson, and D. W. Henderson. 1981. *Applying Nutrients and Other Chemicals to Trickle-irrigated Crops.* Division of agricultural science bulletin 1893. Davis, CA: University of California.

Smajstrla, A. G. 1981. *Designing Trickle Irrigation Systems for Uniformity.* Agricultural engineering extension report 81–7. Gainesville, FL: University of Florida Cooperative Extension.

Smajstrla, A. G., B. J. Boman, G. A. Clark, D. Z. Haman, F. T. Izuno, and F. S. Zazueta. 1988. *Basic Irrigation Scheduling in Florida.* Bulletin 249. Gainesville, FL: University of Florida Cooperative Extension.

Smajstrla, A. G., B. J. Boman, G. A. Clark, D. Z. Haman, D. J. Pitts, and F. S. Zazueta. 1990. *Field Evaluation of Microirrigation Water Application Uniformity.* Bulletin 265. Gainesville, FL: University of Florida Cooperative Extension.

Smajstrla, A. G., G. A. Clark, S. F. Shih, F. S. Zazueta, and D. S. Harrison. 1984a. *Potential Evaporation Probabilities and Distributions in Florida.* Bulletin 205. Gainesville, FL: University of Florida Cooperative Extension.

Smajstrla, A. G., D. Z. Haman, and F. S. Zazueta. 1985c. *Chemical Injection (Chemigation) Methods and Calibration.* Agricultural engineering extension report 85–22. Gainesville, FL: University of Florida Cooperative Extension.

Smajstrla, A. G., D. S. Harrison, W. J. Becker, F. S. Zazueta, and D. Z. Haman. 1985a. *Back Flow Prevention Requirements for Florida Irrigation Systems.* Bulletin 217. Gainesville, FL: University of Florida Cooperative Extension.

Smajstrla, A. G., D. S. Harrison, and G. A. Clark. 1985b. *Trickle Irrigation Scheduling I: Durations of Water Applications.* Bulletin 204. Gainesville, FL: University of Florida Cooperative Extension.

Smajstrla, A. G., D. S. Harrison, J. C. Good, and W. J. Becker. 1984b. *Chemigation Safety.* Agricultural engineering fact sheet AE–28. Gainesville, FL: University of Florida Cooperative Extension.

Smajstrla, A. G., D. S. Harrison, and F. S. Zazueta. 1983b. *Field Evaluation of Trickle Irrigation Systems: Uniformity of Water Application.* Bulletin 195. Gainesville, FL: University of Florida Cooperative Extension.

Smajstrla, A. G., R. C. Koo, J. H. Weldon, D. S. Harrison, and F. S. Zazueta. 1983a. Clogging of trickle irrigation emitters under field conditions. *Proceedings of the Florida State Horticultural Society* 96: 13–17.

Sweeney, D. W., D. A. Graetz, A. B. Bottcher, S. J. Locascio, and K. L. Campbell. 1987. Tomato yield and nitrogen recovery as influenced by irrigation method, nitrogen source, and mulch. *HortScience* 22: 27–29.

Chapter 5: Season-Extension Technology: Row Covers and High Tunnels

Aldrich, R. A. and J. W. Bartok, Jr. 1994. *Greenhouse Engineering.* NRAES–33. Ithaca, NY: Natural Resource, Agriculture and Engineering Service (NRAES).

Bartok, J. W., Jr. 2000. *Greenhouses for Homeowners and Gardeners.* NRAES–137. Ithaca, NY: Natural Resource, Agricultural and Engineering Service (NRAES).

Bonanno, A. R. and W. J. Lamont, Jr. 1987. Effect of polyethylene mulches, irrigation method, and row covers on soil and air temperature and yields of muskmelon. *Journal of the American Society for Horticultural Science* 112: 735–738.

Bornt, C. D., J. B. Loy, W. G. Lord, and O. S. Wells. 1998. Annual strawberry production in New England. *Proceedings of the National Agricultural Plastics Congress* 27: 99–105.

Gent, M. P. N. 1991. *High Tunnels Extend Tomato and Pepper Production.* Bulletin 893. New Haven, CT: The Connecticut Agricultural Experiment Station.

Lamont, W. J., Jr. and M. Orzolek. 2000. *Penn State High Tunnel Research and Education Facility.* University Park, PA: Department of Horticulture, The Pennsylvania State University.

Mansour, N. S. 1993. The use of field covers in vegetable production. *Proceedings of the American Society of Plasticulture*, Heartland Growers Educational Session.

Orozco-Santos, M., J. Farias-Larios, and J. Lopez-Perez. 1999. Effect of floating row cover and transparent mulch on soil temperature and the growth, flowering, and yields of cantaloupe. *Proceedings of the National Agricultural Plastics Congress* 28: 116–121.

Webb, S. E. and S. B. Linda. 1992. Evaluation of spunbonded polyethylene row covers as a method of excluding insects and viruses affecting fall-grown squash in Florida. *Journal of Economic Entomology* 85 (6): 2344–2352.

Wells, O. S. 1996. Rowcover and high tunnel growing systems in the United States. *HortTechnology* 6 (3): 172–176. Wells, O. S. and J. B. Loy. 1985. Intensive vegetable production with row covers. *HortScience* 20: 822–826.

Chapter 6: Windbreaks

Baker, Kissida, and Gould. *Trees in the Landscape.* Bulletin 183. College Park, MD: University of Maryland.

Brandle, J. R., B. B. Johnson, and T. Akeson. 1992. Field windbreaks: Are they economical? *Journal of Production Agriculture* 5: 393–398.

Franklin D. Schales and Robert J. Rouse. 1980. Effect of windbreaks type and location of protection of plastic mulched muskmelon. *Proceedings of the 15th National Agricultural Plastics Congress,* 100–103.

Greig et al. 1974. Residual effects of wind- and sandblast-damage on tomato plants at different stages of development. *Journal of the American Society for Horticultural Science* 99: 530–534.

Hodges, L. and J. R. Brandle. 1996. Windbreaks: An important component in a plasticulture system. *HortTechnology* 6 (3): 177–181.

Kissida, Pitt, and Gould. *Plants for Windbreaks.* Publication no. LDF-78-02. College Park, MD: University of Maryland.

Lorenz, D. G., W. C. Sharp, and J. D. Ruffner. 1991. *Conservation Plants for the Northeast.* Bulletin 1154. Washington, DC: Soil Conservation Service, United States Department of Agriculture.

North Carolina Strawberry Association. *The Strawberry Grower* 5 (10).

Pitt, Kissida, and Gould. *Residential Landscape Design for Wind Control.* Publication no. LDF 78-01. College Park, MD: University of Maryland.

Rutgers—The State University of New Jersey. 1999. *Commercial Vegetable Production Recommendation for Maryland, Pennsylvania, New Jersey, Delaware, and Virginia.* New Brunswick, NJ: Rutgers—The State University of New Jersey.

Schultheis, Jonathan R. 1995 (March). *Commercial Watermelon Production.* Horticultural information leaflet 30. Raleigh, NC: North Carolina State University.

Sustainable Agriculture Network. 1998. *Managing Cover Crops Profitability.* Second edition. Beltsville, MD: Sustainable Agriculture Network.

Tjaden, Robert and Glenda Weber. *Riparian Buffer Management Grasses for Riparian Buffers and Wildlife Habitat Improvement.* Fact sheet 728. College Park, MD: University of Maryland.

Tjaden, Robert and Glenda Weber. *Riparian Buffer Management Trees for Riparian Forest Buffers.* Fact sheet 726. College Park, MD: University of Maryland.

United States Department of Agriculture. *Windbreaks for Conservation.* Bulletin 339. Washington, DC: United States Department of Agriculture.

University of Maryland. 1999. *Maryland Commercial Small Fruit Production Guide.* College Park, MD: University of Maryland.

Chapter 7: Crop Establishment Options— Machinery and Spacings for Plasticulture

Bennett, M. A. and E. M. Grassbaugh. 1992. Influence of transplant characteristics on processing tomato seedling development and yields. *Proceedings of the Third National Symposium on Stand Establishment of Horticultural Crops* 101: 301–310.

Bennett, M. A. and E. M. Grassbaugh. 1995. Cell size and starter fertilizer effects on processing bell pepper transplant growth, crop establishment and yield. *Proceedings of the Fourth National Symposium on Stand Establishment of Horticultural Crops* 4: 161–168.

Beverly, R. B., J. G. Latimer, and R. D. Oetting. 1992. Effects of root cell size and brushing on transplant growth and field establishment of 'Sunrise' tomato under a line-source irrigation variable. *Proceedings of the Third National Symposium on Stand Establishment of Horticultural Crops* 101: 249–258.

Brown, J. E. 1991. Mulches, row covers, and soil solarization for vegetable crops. CRIS report. United States Department of Agriculture.

Fisher, K. J. and A. P. Julian. 1988. Some effects of delayed planting of tomato cell transplants on later crop performance. *Proceedings of the First National Symposium on Stand Establishment of Horticultural Crops* 1: 156–162.

Garton, R. W. 1992. Field performance of 406 cell tomato transplants. *Proceedings of the Third National Symposium on Stand Establishment of Horticultural Crops* 101: 295–299.

Hayslip, N. C. 1973. Plug-mix seeding developments in Florida. *Proceedings of the Florida State Horticultural Society* 86: 179–185.

Inman, J. W. 1995. New developments in planting and transplanting equipment. *Proceedings of the Fourth National Symposium on Stand Establishment of Horticultural Crops* 4: 19–21.

Jones, R. T. 1994. *Historical Supplement to the Proceedings of the 25th National Agricultural Plastics Congress.* Lexington, KY.

Khan, V. A., C. Stevens, J. Y. Lu, D. J. Collins, M. A. Wilson, J. E. Brown, M. K. Kabwe, and O. Adeyeye. 1993. Response of okra transplants grown on soil solarizing plots during the active period of soil solarization. *Proceedings of the National Agricultural Plastics Congress* 24: 162–169.

Marr, C. W. and W. J. Lamont, Jr. 1990. Plastic mulches to establish seedling asparagus transplants. *HortScience* 25 (12): 1661.

NeSmith, D. S. 1992. Transplant age influences establishment and growth of 'Dixie' summer squash. *Proceedings of the Third National Symposium on Stand Establishment of Horticultural Crops* 101: 265–277.

NeSmith, D. S. 1994. Transplant age has little influence on yield of muskmelon *(Cucumis melo L.). HortScience* 29 (8): 916.

Ng, T. J. and F. D. Schales. 1978. Effect of cultivar, plant density and soil fertility upon yield and quality of muskmelon on black polyethylene mulch. *Proceedings of the National Agricultural Plastics Congress* 14: 199–205.

Olson, S. M. 1999. Personal communication.

Orzolek, M. D. 1991. Stand establishment of vegetables in the field. *HortTechnology* 1 (1): 78–81.

Orzolek, M. D and D. R. Daum. 1984. Effect of planting equipment and techniques on seed germination and emergence: A review. *Journal of Seed Technology* 9 (2): 99–113.

Orzolek, M. D and D. R. Daum. 1986. *Planters for Seeding Vegetables.* Agricultural engineering fact sheet PM–87. University Park, PA: The Pennsylvania State University.

Shaw, L. N. 1987. Engineering aspects of crop establishment through plastic mulch. *Proceedings of the National Agricultural Plastics Congress* 20: 232–239.

Shaw, L. N. 1988. A look at automatic transplanting. *Proceedings of the First International Symposium on Stand Establishment for Horticultural Crops* 1: 185–191.

Shaw, L. N., H. H. Bryan, and J. W. Mishoe. 1978. Double cropping mulch covered beds. *Proceedings of the National Agricultural Plastics Congress* 14: 222–226.

Vavrina, C. S. and M. D. Orzolek. 1993. Tomato transplant age: A review. *HortTechnology* 3 (3): 313–316.

Vavrina, C. S., K. D. Shuler, and P. R. Gilreath. 1994. Evaluating the impact of transplanting depth on bell pepper growth and yield. *HortScience* 29 (10): 1133–1135.

Wilson, M. A., V. A. Khan, and C. Stevens. 1993. Influence of several plastic mulches with four row covers on yield of 'Crimson Sweet' watermelons in southeast Missouri. *Proceedings of the National Agricultural Plastics Congress* 24: 209–214.

Chapter 8:
Weed Management in Plasticulture

Abdul-Baki, A., J. R. Teasdale, and D. R. Korsak. 1997. Nitrogen requirements of fresh market tomatoes on hairy vetch and black polyethylene mulch. *HortScience* 32: 217–221.

Ashley, R. A. 1997. Critical period for weed control in peppers on black plastic. *Proceedings of the New England Vegetable and Berry Conference*, 62–63.

Bonanno, A. R. 1986. Evaluation of herbicides for use between plastic mulch in cucurbit and solanaceous crop production. *Proceedings of the National Agricultural Plastics Congress* 19: 339–347.

Bonanno, A. R. 1987. Influence of oxyfluorfen and cinmethylin on weed control, yield, and quality of tomatoes grown in plastic culture. *Proceedings of the Southern Weed Science Society* 40: 121.

Bonanno, A. R. 1988. Influence of oxyfluorfen, cinmethylin, and glufosinate on weed control, yield, and quality of pepper. *Proceedings of the Weed Science Society of America* 28: 70.

Bonanno, A. R. 1989. Influence of oxyfluorfen, cinmethylin, ethalfluralin, and glufosinate on weed control and yield of muskmelons grown in plastic culture. *Proceedings of the Weed Science Society of America* 29: 26–27.

Bonanno, A. R. 1991. Avoiding herbicide injury on supersweets. *American Vegetable Grower* April: 42–44.

Bonanno, A. R. 1999. Common weed management problems facing New England vegetable and small fruit growers. *Proceedings of the Northeastern Weed Science Society* 53: 86.

Bonanno, A. R. and W. J. Lamont. 1985. The effect of polyethylene mulches and row covers on yield of muskmelons in North Carolina. *Proceedings of the National Agricultural Plastics Congress* 18: 48–55.

Bonanno, A. R. and W. J. Lamont. 1987. The effect of polyethylene mulches and row covers on yield of muskmelon. *Journal of the American Society for Horticultural Science* 112:735–738.

Bowman, G. (ed.) 1997. *Steel in the Field: A Farmer's Guide to Weed Management.* Burlington, VT: Sustainable Agriculture Network, University of Vermont.

Else, M. J. 1995. Personal communication. Amherst, MA: UMass Extension.

Gilreath, J. P. 1986. Photodegradation of paraquat applied to polyethylene film mulch. *Proceedings of the Southern Weed Science Society* 39: 178.

Gilreath, J. P. 1987. Photodegradation of glyphosate: Effect on tomato transplants. *Proceedings of the Southern Weed Science Society* 40: 126.

Grubinger, V. and M. J. Else. 1995. *Vegetable Growers and Their Weed Control Machines* (video). Burlington, VT: University of Vermont.

Monaco, T. J. and A. R. Bonanno. 1985. Herbicide evaluations in horticultural crops. *North Carolina State University Horticultural Crops Research Series* 72: 1–226.

Motsenbocker, C. E. and A. R. Bonanno. 1988. The influence of herbicides on the growth and yield of muskmelons *(Cucumis melo L.)* grown with plastic mulches and row covers. *Weed Science* 36: 234–238.

Motsenbocker, C. E. and A. R. Bonanno. 1989. The influence of plastic mulches, row covers, and herbicides on the growth and yield of muskmelons *(Cucumis melo). HortScience* 24: 601–603.

Chapter 10:
Production of Strawberries Using Plasticulture

Darrow, G. M. 1966. *The Strawberry: History, Breeding, and Physiology.* New York: Holt, Rinehart & Winston.

Fiola, J. A. 1999 (February). Our latest technology in strawberry plasticulture. *Proceedings of the North American Strawberry Growers Association Annual Meeting.*

Fiola, J. A. 1999. *A Partial List of Strawberry Plants for Plasticulture.* Fact sheet. Cream Ridge, NJ: Rutgers Cooperative Extension.

Funt, R. C. et al. 1985. *Ohio Strawberry Manual.* Bulletin 436. Columbus, OH: Ohio State University Extension.

Maas, J. L. 1998. *Compendium of Strawberry Diseases.* Second edition. St. Paul, MN: APS Press.

O'Dell, C. and J. Williams. 1995. *Fall Planted Hill System Plasticulture Strawberry Production Guide for Virginia.* Blacksburg, VA: Virginia Cooperative Extension.

Poling, E. B. 1996. Monitoring plant development and crop forecasting. In *The Chandler Notebook.* Raleigh, NC: North Carolina Strawberry Association.

Poling, E. B. and D. W. Monks. 1994. *Strawberry Plasticulture Guide for North Carolina.* Bulletin AG-515. Raleigh, NC: North Carolina Cooperative Extension Service.

Poling, E. B. and K. Parker. 1990. Plug production of strawberry transplants. *Advances in Strawberry Production* 9: 7–39.

Pritts, M. and D. Handley. 1998. *Strawberry Production Guide for the Northeast, Midwest, and Eastern Canada.* NRAES–88. Ithaca, NY: Natural Resource, Agriculture, and Engineering Service (NRAES).

Chapter 11:
Specialty Cut-Flower Plasticulture

Armitage, Alan. 1993. *Specialty Cut Flowers.* Portland, OR: Timber Press.

Association of Specialty Cut Flower Growers. *The Cut Flower Quarterly.* Oberlin, OH: Association of Specialty Cut Flower Growers.

Growing for Market. Monthly newsletter covering many small-farm issues; very strong in cut flower production and marketing. Lawrence, KS: Fairplain Publications. <www.growingformarket.com>

Kuhns, Larry J., Tracey Harpster, Jim Sellmer, and Scott Guiser. 1997. *Controlling Weeds in Nursery and Landscape Plantings.* University Park, PA: Penn State Cooperative Extension Service.

Stevens, Alan B. 1998. *Field Grown Cut Flowers: A Practical Guide and Sourcebook: Commercial Field Grown Fresh and Dried Cut Flower Production.* Edgerton, WI: Avatar's World.

Chapter 12:
Managing Used Agricultural Plastics

The province of Ontario, Canada, has had an agricultural plastic recycling pilot program for several years with some success. For further information and some fact sheets on the program, contact:

Ontario Ministry of Agriculture and Food
Toll-free phone: (877) 424-1300
Local phone: (519) 826-4047
E-mail: ag.info@omaf.gov.on.ca
Web site: www.gov.on.ca/omafra/

For further information on emissions and health effects of open burning of plastics, environmental liability of on-farm dumping, as well as general information on plastics used in agricultural applications, contact the chapter author for a fact sheet listing:

James W. Garthe, PE
Department of Agricultural and Biological Engineering
246 Agricultural Engineering Building
University Park, PA 16802
Phone: (814) 865-7154
Fax: (814) 863-1031
E-mail: jwg10@psu.edu

Amidon, A. 1992. Recycling agricultural plastics. *Resource Recycling* (January 1992): 1–26.

Bonhotal, J. 1997. *Agricultural Plastics—Boon or Bane?* Fact sheet. Ithaca, NY: Department of Agricultural and Biological Engineering, Cornell University.

Elomaa, M. and E. Saharinen. 1991. Polycyclic aromatic hydrocarbons (PAHs) in soot produced by combustion of polystyrene, polypropylene, and wood. *Journal of Applied Polymer Science* 42: 2819–2824.

Lemieux, P. M. 1997. *Evaluation of Emissions from the Open Burning of Household Waste in Barrels.* Volume 1, technical report no. EPA-600/R-97-134a. Washington, DC: United States Environmental Protection Agency, Office of Research and Development.

Lemieux, P. M., C. C. Lutes, J. A. Abbott, and K. M. Aldous. 2000. Emissions of polychlorinated dibenzo-p-dioxins and polychlorinated dibenzofurans from the open burning of household waste in barrels. *American Chemical Society's Environmental Science and Technology* ASAP (as soon as publishable) article released on the World Wide Web January 4, 2000.

Linak, W. P., E. Perry, R. W. Williams, J. V. Ryan, and D. M. DeMarini. 1989. Chemical and biological characterization of products of incomplete combustion from the simulated field burning of agricultural plastic. *International Journal of Air Pollution Control and Waste Management* (JAPCA) 39: 836–846.

Negra, C. and G. Rogers. 1998. *Agricultural Plastic Recycling: Investigation of Opportunities and Obstacles in Vermont.* Burlington, VT: University of Vermont Extension.

Negra, C. and N. Starr. 1997. *Plastic Agricultural Film Recycling: A Cooperative Feasibility Study for Three New England States.* Burlington, VT: University of Vermont Extension.

Patrick Engineering, Inc. and Two Rivers Regional Council of Public Officials. 1994. *Emission Characteristics of Burn Barrels.* Washington, DC: United States Environmental Protection Agency, Region V.

Rathje, William and Cullen Murphy. 1992. *Rubbish! The Archaeology of Garbage.* New York: HarperCollins Publishers, Inc.

Other Books from NRAES

The books below can be ordered from NRAES (Natural Resource, Agriculture, and Engineering Service). Complete book descriptions are posted on the NRAES Web site. The Web page address for each book is given below its description. Before ordering, contact NRAES for current prices and shipping and handling charges, or for a free catalog.

NRAES, Cooperative Extension
PO Box 4557
Ithaca, New York 14852-4557
Phone: (607) 255-7654
Fax: (607) 254-8770
E-mail: NRAES@CORNELL.EDU
Web site: WWW.NRAES.ORG

BRAMBLE PRODUCTION GUIDE

NRAES–35 • 189 pages • 1989
ISBN 0-935817-21-2

Includes in-depth coverage of all aspects of raspberry and blackberry production, including site preparation, plant selection, water and nutrient management, pest management, marketing, and more. Color photos help identify pests and diagnose diseases. Intended for growers, their advisors, and educators.

Features
- 115 color photos
- 37 figures
- 47 tables

WWW.NRAES.ORG/PUBLICATIONS/NRAES35.HTML

GREENHOUSE ENGINEERING

NRAES–33 • 212 pages • 1994
ISBN 0-935817-57-3

Eight chapters and 13 appendixes include information needed to plan, construct, and manage a commercial greenhouse. Types of structures, materials handling equipment, environmental control, remodeling, and energy conservation are discussed. Intended for growers, designers, educators, and students.

Features
- 105 illustrations
- 38 tables
- Sample calculations

WWW.NRAES.ORG/PUBLICATIONS/NRAES33.HTML

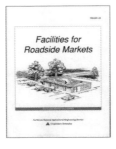

FACILITIES FOR ROADSIDE MARKETS

NRAES–52 • 32 pages • 1992

Discusses site evaluation (visibility, accessibility, utilities, drainage, and building ordinances); market layout (areas for sales, preparation, and shipping and receiving); structures; parking; lighting; and more. Useful to those who are looking to start, improve, or expand a roadside market.

Features
- 26 illustrations
- Two sets of plans
- Sign guidelines

WWW.NRAES.ORG/PUBLICATIONS/NRAES52.HTML

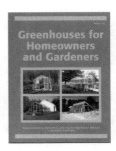

GREENHOUSES FOR HOMEOWNERS AND GARDENERS

NRAES–137 • 200 pages • 2000
ISBN 0-935817-51-4

Eight chapters cover selecting a greenhouse plan or kit, construction planning, framing materials, glazing, layouts, equipment, environmental control, window greenhouses, growth chambers, and garden structures. Useful to gardeners, homeowners, educators, small farmers, retirement homes, schools, and other institutions.

Features
- 150+ line drawings
- Sample calculations
- Greenhouse plans

WWW.NRAES.ORG/PUBLICATIONS/NRAES137.HTML

(More books on next page)

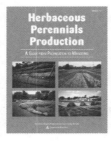

HERBACEOUS PERENNIALS PRODUCTION: A GUIDE FROM PROPAGATION TO MARKETING

NRAES–93 • 208 pages • 1998
ISBN 0-935817-29-8

Provides practical management information, including propagation methods for over 900 species, germination conditions for over 400 species, and common pest problems for over 400 species. Discusses several production systems and much more. Intended for growers, their advisors, and educators.

Features
- **37 illustrations**
- **45 tables**
- **Glossary**

WWW.NRAES.ORG/PUBLICATIONS/NRAES93.HTML

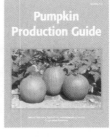

PUMPKIN PRODUCTION GUIDE

NRAES–123 • 152 pages • 2003
ISBN 0-935817-83-2

Covers production basics and cutting-edge research. Provides in-depth coverage of all aspects of production, including site preparation, variety selection, cultural practices, fruit set and pollination, pest management, marketing, and more. Color photos help identify pests and diagnose diseases. For growers, their advisors, serious gardeners, and educators.

Features
- **116 color photos**
- **21 figures**
- **Key to diseases**

WWW.NRAES.ORG/PUBLICATIONS/NRAES123.HTML

HIGHBUSH BLUEBERRY PRODUCTION GUIDE

NRAES–55 • 200 pages • 1992

Includes in-depth coverage of all aspects of highbush blueberry production, including site preparation, plant selection, water and nutrient management, pest management, marketing, and more. Color photos help identify pests and diagnose diseases. Intended for growers, their advisors, and educators.

Features
- **168 color photos**
- **24 figures**
- **27 tables**

WWW.NRAES.ORG/PUBLICATIONS/NRAES55.HTML

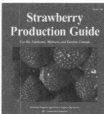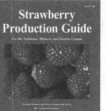

STRAWBERRY PRODUCTION GUIDE FOR THE NORTHEAST, MIDWEST, AND EASTERN CANADA

NRAES–88 • 162 pages • 1998
ISBN 0-935817-23-9

Includes in-depth coverage of all aspects of production, including site preparation, plant selection, water and nutrient management, pest management, marketing, and more. Color photos help identify pests and diagnose diseases. Intended for growers, their advisors, and educators.

Features
- **115 color photos**
- **37 figures**
- **47 tables**

WWW.NRAES.ORG/PUBLICATIONS/NRAES88.HTML

ON-FARM COMPOSTING HANDBOOK

NRAES–54 • 186 pages • 1992
ISBN 0-935817-19-0

Internationally recognized, practical book discusses large-scale composting, including raw materials, methods, equipment, management, marketing, and more. Includes worksheets, forms, and references. Intended for persons interested in large-scale composting, this book is also use as a college text.

Features
- **56 illustrations**
- **32 tables**
- **22,000+ sold**

WWW.NRAES.ORG/PUBLICATIONS/NRAES54.HTML

SUSTAINABLE VEGETABLE PRODUCTION FROM START-UP TO MARKET

NRAES–104 • 268 pages • 1999
ISBN 0-935817-45-X

Reviews all phases of moderate-scale vegetable production, including business management, marketing, crop rotation, cover crops, equipment, crop handling, pest management, and more. Intended for new and experienced growers, educators, and serious gardeners. Used as a college text.

Features
- **32 grower profiles**
- **91 illustrations**
- **Enterprise budgets**

WWW.NRAES.ORG/PUBLICATIONS/NRAES104.HTML